AMERICAN
SEA SONGS
AND
CHANTEYS

AMERICAN SEA SONGS

AND

CHANTEYS

from the days of

Iron Men and Wooden Ships

By FRANK SHAY

Illustrated by
EDWARD A. WILSON

Musical Arrangements by
CHRISTOPHER THOMAS

W · W · NORTON & COMPANY · INC · *New York*

ALL RIGHTS RESERVED

PRINTED IN THE UNITED STATES OF AMERICA
FOR THE PUBLISHERS BY THE VAIL-BALLOU PRESS

IN TRIBUTE
TO
NATHANIEL BOWDITCH
MATTHEW FONTAINE MAURY
DONALD McKAY

Contents

CHANTEYS

7

FORECASTLE SONGS

WARDROOM BALLADS

MISCELLANEOUS SONGS AND BALLADS

Introduction

IN THE DAYS of iron men and wooden ships, when the motive power was human muscle and white canvas, it was the custom of American sailors to ease their work and their leisure with song. The songs they sang were the songs of their craft, chanteys and ballads of the sea. It is conceivable that at the beginning of a voyage the tailor-made songs of the shore enjoyed some favor, but sooner or later they were forgotten and the crew returned to their own melodies.

The work song, which we spell "chantey" and pronounce "shanty," was of the sailors' own making. The rhythm was supplied by the task; the words had to fit whether they made sense or not, and only too often had meanings known only to the sailors of the day. The wording was simple, direct, and the music often had a wild, spirited quality, salty as the sea and as rough as the waves in a storm. The songs were designed to lighten certain back-breaking tasks: the chorus lines, on which action was based, became rigid and changeless, but the solo lines were always at the mercy of the chanteyman and improvisation and parody were frequent. In singing, the chanteyman, who also put his back to the task, would sound off:

> CHANTEYMAN: When I come ashore and get my pay,
> CREW: Walk with me, Miss Edie, *do!*
> CHANTEYMAN: On that bright and always sunny day,
> CREW: Oh, my Edie, walk with me, *do!*

the final word in the chorus line being the signal for the men to fall back on the rope. There was much repetition and many verses, though, as a short job song, a very few verses served for a task.

The chantey, though English in origin, early became American in content. The New York packets, beginning in 1818 with the famous Black Ball Line, brought the chantey into efficient use. These ships sailed on schedule; that is, they left their ports on stated dates and tried to make the fastest passage possible. To achieve this end the ships and their crews had to be driven, full sail was carried day and night, through fair weather and foul. The old methods of securing prompt action from the crew—a foul oath, a blow of the fist, or a taste of the rope's end—could not be employed in the presence of polite passengers. The work song became the rule, and a really good chanteyman was worth four men in a watch. Dana says, in *Two Years Before the Mast:* "A song is as necessary to sailors as the drum and fife to a soldier. They must pull together as soldiers must step in time, and they can't pull in time, or pull with a will, without it. Many a time, when a thing goes heavy, one fellow yo-ho-ing a lively song, like 'Heave, to the Girls!,' 'Nancy, O!,' 'Jack Crosstree,' 'Cheer'ly man,' has put life and strength into every arm."

Roughly the chanteys may be divided into three classes: capstan and windlass chanteys, used in catting or weighing anchor or hoisting sails; the halliard or long-drag chantey, used at topsails and topgallant sails; and the sheet, tack, and bowline songs, known as short-drag chanteys. Others, such as walkaways, hand-over-hand and pumping chanteys were, as a rule, adaptations of other work songs and ballads.

It is a mistake to think that the chantey went out with the full-rigged sailing ship; the old sailors went into steam, reluctantly it is true, and they took their gear and their songs with them. The newer men heard the songs and passed them on, even if they found little practical use for them. In steam there was no heavy heaving; steam did the work, and steam sings its own song. Though most of the back-breaking tasks were gone, the singers came and passed and the songs stayed on because of their character and charm and today are sung with as great enthusiasm as in the old days.

The songs of leisure were usually the story-ballads that followed closely the pattern of shore folk song: they honored woman, home, ships and battles, sobriety and the lack of it, and they deplored hard work, poor grub, and harsh treatment. Some of these songs were tailor-made and, contrary to general opinion, were liked and sung by sailors, especially those of the Navy. In fact, most Navy songs show the hand of the scrivener in rhyme and meter. There was no chanteying it up in the service, where all work was done in silence and in response to the boatswain's pipe. But in the wardrooms and at the scuttle butt much time was given to singing.

The old merchant sailors were not all the stupid oafs or the fools they have been pictured who, once ashore, got drunk and remained that way until their money was spent. There were plenty of that type, but there were many who, like Reuben Ranzo, studied navigation and made their way to the quarterdeck and eventual command of their own vessels. Many had families and hurried home as soon as their ships made port. They took care of themselves and when the wintry winds began to blow, when going aloft meant flirting with sudden death, exerted every effort to get shore jobs for the winter. Some went into the southern cotton packets for a voyage to Mobile or New Orleans; others went into the railway construction gangs, some to northern lumber camps. All these changes influenced their songs.

Many of the sailors' songs were and still are beautiful and an experience to hear. There is no song in the world quite like "Shenandoah," a capstan chantey that was also a favorite between watches. Its haunting melody was seldom heard ashore. "The Dreadnought," "The Yankee Man-of-War," "Home, Dearie, Home," and "Rolling Home" will live as long as men have voices to sing.

For all his rowdiness, his traditional use of profanity, the old sailor's songs for the most part remained unsullied while they stayed at sea. They closely followed the pattern of the singer's own life: he was clean and sober at sea and something else ashore. Yet some of the songs, beginning with simple decent verses, eventually wound up in obscenity. Shore songs have the same tendency.

Those of us who have heard the chanteys sung in their native habitat are often distressed by the efforts of shorebirds to animate them: most sound as though they were hillbilly ballads, which they emphatically are not. There is a rollicking, exuberant quality that is found in no other music—the rhythmic straining of human muscle, of hard breathing, of work going well, measured by sea legs and emitted from lungs filled with the salt sea air. But, as has been pointed out, the tasks that brought them into being are now gone and all must be sung without the original maritime activities.

There is an old Spanish story of a man loafing on the shore who saw a ship drawing near its wharf. The old sailorman at the wheel sang a wondrous sweet song, and, going to the pier, the idler asked him to repeat it, but the old sailor replied:

> "I can sing the song to no one,
> Save to him who sails with me."

Acknowledgments

I HEARD my first chantey in 1915 while serving as a foremast hand aboard the tanker *Standard*. She took fire off Yucatan and her entire power plant was burned out; all subsequent work had to be done by hand. Another ship stood by to take us in tow, and heavy hawse lines were passed, only to part, and repassed, all handled by the small crew. Work was going poorly until a shipmate sounded off with "Whiskey for My Johnny." The song brought immediate results and others were broken out, mostly in fragments. By the time the *Standard* made port I had a small collection of the old chanteys: subsequent voyages increased my repertory.

The names of those shipmates and of the sailors met in shore traps have long been forgotten, but their songs have not nor have my recollections of a fine body of men. Certain shorebirds and sailors-who-have-swallowed-the-anchor have, during the intervening years, aided in the collection of my material. Grateful acknowledgment is made to Paul Chavchavadze, C. D. Harvey, Harry Kemp, Christopher Morley, William McFee, Eugene O'Neill and Charles B. Palmer for both material help and enthusiasm.

To Miss Joanna C. Colcord for permission to include material from her admirable *Songs of American Sailormen*.

To Arch H. Ferguson, of Brown, Son & Ferguson, Ltd., Glasgow, for selections from *Sea Songs and Shanties*, by Captain W. B. Whall.

To Duncan Emrich, chief of the Folklore Section, and to the staff of the Library of Congress.

To Harvard University Library, the New York Public Library, the Public Library of the City of Boston, and to the Wellfleet Public Library.

My indebtedness to my distinguished collaborators, Mr. Edward A. Wilson and Mr. Christopher Thomas is evident on every page of this book.

And to my wife, Edith Shay, for constant and painstaking aid and encouragement.

F.S.

FIDELITY

Chanteys

Away, Rio!

SAILING DAY for a famous clipper was always a gala affair. All the great ships had their fans who followed their careers, cheered their speedy passages, and often welcomed them home. But sailing day attracted the greatest crowds. In New York the ships were loaded at their East River wharves and then dropped down to the Battery to await the tide, to take on tardy foremast hands, and to receive final orders.

It was the first mate's day, it was his show and he knew that his future rating would be determined by the smart manner in which he got his vessel to sea. The sailors were not insensible to the drama of the moment and, drunk or sober, wanted to make the most of it. Captain and pilot were on the quarter-deck, with the captain's eye on his chronometer; the mate was on the forecastle, with his eye on the captain. As the tide prepares to ebb, the order is passed forward and the chief officer goes into action and snaps out his order: "Now, men and sogers both, heave away at the windlass. You, chanteyman, give us 'Rye-O!' and raise the decks, aye, raise the very dead. Heave and a-way!" And the rollin' bollin' words of the best of all outward-bound chanteys rolls across the water and brings cheers from the shorebirds.

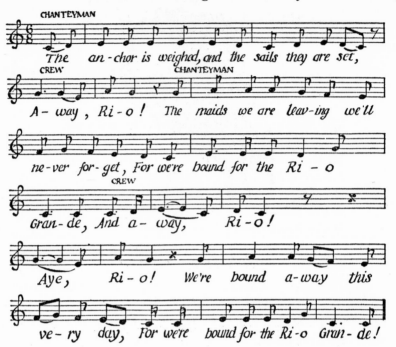

The anchor is weighed, and the sails they are set,
Away, Rio!
The maids we are leaving we'll never forget,
For we're bound for the Rio Grande,
And away, Rio! Aye, Rio!
We're bound away this very day,
For we're bound for the Rio Grande!

So it's pack up your donkey and get under way,
The girls we are leaving can take our half pay.

We've a jolly good ship and a jolly good crew,
A jolly good mate and a good skipper, too.

We'll sing as we heave to the maidens we leave,
And you who are listening, good-by to you.

Heave with a will and heave long and strong,
Sing the good chorus, for 'tis a good song.

Heave only one pawl, then 'vast heavin', belay!
Heave steady, because we say farewell today.

The chain's up and down, now the bosun did say,
Away, Rio!
Heave up to the hawsepipe, the anchor's aweigh.
For we're bound for the Rio Grande,
And away, Rio! Aye, Rio!
We're bound away this very day,
We're bound for the Rio Grande!

Once the anchor is apeak, the chief mate turns to the quarter-deck and, receiving his orders from the captain, cries: "Lay aloft there, ye walkin' corpses, and loose all sails!" The second and third mates, the bosun, and the bosun's mate rush to their stations, repeating orders and checking the progress of the work. But the first mate's men had the jump and the foremast is the first to break out white, followed quickly and in decent order by the main and mizzen masts. Other chanteys break out, and from the shore comes another great cheer that puts even more heart and brawn into the crew. The pilot goes to the helm, the ship moves, and a new voyage has begun.

Sally Brown

THERE WERE a lot of girls in Jack's shore life, but Sally Brown was the belle of them all. To her were attributed all the virtues of a good wife and all the vices of a strumpet. Although she hailed from New York City, she was seen in almost every port and was as great a favorite with the English as with Americans. Often she was sung to more cozily and intimately than in the present version, which was used as a capstan chantey.

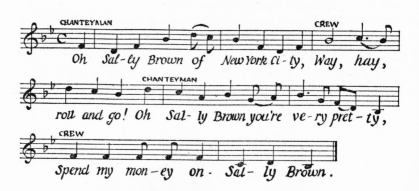

Oh, Sally Brown, of New York City,
Way, hay, roll and go!
Oh, Sally Brown you're very pretty,
Spend my money on Sally Brown!

24

Oh, Sally Brown's a bright mulatto,
 Way, hay, roll and go!
She drinks rum and chews tobacco,
 Spend my money on Sally Brown!

Oh, Sally Brown's a Creole lady,
 Way, hay, roll and go!
She's the mother of a yellow baby,
 Spend my money on Sally Brown!

Seven long years I courted Sally,
 Way, hay, roll and go!
Sweetest girl in all the valley,
 Spend my money on Sally Brown!

Seven long years and she wouldn't marry,
 Way, hay, roll and go!
And I no longer cared to tarry,
 Spend my money on Sally Brown!

So I courted Sal, her only daughter,
 Way, hay, roll and go!
For her I sail upon the water,
 Spend my money on Sally Brown!

Sally's teeth are white and pearly,
 Way, hay, roll and go!
Her eyes are blue, her hair is curly,
 Spend my money on Sally Brown!

Now my troubles are all over,
 Way, hay, roll and go!
Sally's married to a dirty soldier,
 Spend my money on Sally Brown!

The Dead Horse

WHEN A SAILOR shipped aboard a vessel for a new voyage, he was often in debt to his boardinghouse, his tavern, or to the owners for clothing and gear. This debt, called the "horse," had to be worked out before he was again on the receiving end. When he was free and clear of the debt, his horse was said to be dead.

They say old man your horse will die,
And they say so and they hope so.
Oh, poor old man your horse will die,
Oh, poor old man!

For thirty * days I've ridden him,
And they say so, and they hope so.
And when he dies we'll tan his skin,
Oh, poor old man!

And if he lives, I'll ride him again,
And they say so, and they hope so.
I'll ride him with a tighter rein.
Oh, poor old horse!

It's up aloft the horse must go,
They say so, and they hope so.
We'll hoist him up and bury him low.
Oh, poor old horse!

* or sixty or ninety days.

Five Short-Drag Chanteys

THE SHORT-DRAG CHANTEY is the oldest form of sailors' work songs and to modern ears probably the least entertaining. They were, as the title indicates, used in short, quick hauls, when the fore, main, or crossjack sheets were hauled aft and the bowlines tautened and made fast. "Haul on the Bowline" is reputedly the oldest of all chanteys, dating from the time of England's Henry the Eighth. Modern usage has enlivened "Haul Away, Joe!"

Haul on the Bowline

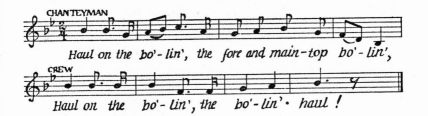

Haul on the bo'-lin', the fore and main-top bo'-lin',
Haul on the bo'-lin', the bo'-lin' · haul!

Haul on the bo'lin', the fore and maintop bo'lin',
  Haul on the bo'lin', the bo'lin' *haul!*
Haul on the bo'lin', the packet is a-rollin',
Haul on the bo'lin', the skipper he's a-growlin',
Haul on the bo'lin', to London we are goin',
Haul on the bo'lin', the good ship is a-bowlin',
Haul on the bo'lin', the main-topgallant bo'lin',
  Haul on the bo'lin', the bo'lin' *haul!*

Johnny Boker

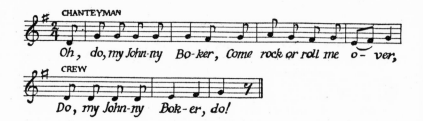

Oh, do, my Johnny Boker,
Come rock or roll me over,
Do, my Johnny Boker, do!

Oh, do, my Johnny Boker,
They say that you're no rover,
Do, my Johnny Boker, do!

Oh, do, my Johnny Boker,
I'm bound away to leave you,
Do, my Johnny Boker, do!

Boney

Boney was a warrior,
  Away-ay, ah!
A warrior, a terrier,
  Jean Francois!

Boney beat the Prussians,
Then he licked the Russians.

Boney went to Waterlow,
There he got his overthrow.

He went to Saint Helena,
  Away-ay, ah!
There he was a prisoner,
  Jean Francois!

Haul Away, Joe

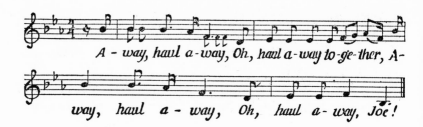

A - way, haul a - way, Oh, haul a - way to-ge-ther, A-
way, haul a - way, Oh, haul a - way, Joe!

Away, haul away, Oh, haul away together,
Away, haul away, Oh, haul away, Joe!

When I was a little lad, my mother told me,
Away, haul away, Oh, haul away together,
That if I did not kiss the girls my lips would grow moldy
Away, haul away, Oh, haul away, Joe!

So first I had a Spanish girl but she was fat and lazy.
Away, haul away, Oh, haul away together,
But now I've got an Irish girl and she nearly drives me crazy.
Away, haul away, Oh, haul away, Joe!

Away, haul away, Oh, haul away together,
Away, haul away, Oh, haul away, Joe!

Another version goes:

> King Louie was the king of France,
> Before the riv-*vi*-lution!

> Then he got his head cut off,
> Which spiled his cons-*ti*-tution!

Paddy Doyle

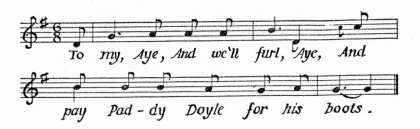

To my, Aye, And we'll furl, Aye, And

pay Pad - dy Doyle for his boots.

To my,
    Aye,
And we'll *furl*,
    Aye,
And pay Paddy Doyle for his *boots*.

We'll *sing*,
    Aye,
And we'll *heave*,
    Aye,
And we'll hang Paddy Doyle for his *boots*.

We'll *heave*,
    Aye,
With a *swing*,
    Aye,
And we'll all drink brandy and *gin*.

Cheer'ly, Man

THIS IS a long-drag chantey and is probably another version of the chantey used in catting the anchor mentioned by Dana in *Two Years Before the Mast*. The verses heard today are a bit more intimate and reveal to a greater degree the charms of the ladies mentioned.

Oh, Nancy Dawson, hio!
   Cheer'ly, man!
She's got a notion, hio!
   Cheer'ly, man!
For our old bosun, hio!
   Cheer'ly, man,
   Oh! hauley, hio!
   Cheer'ly, man!

Oh, Betsy Baker, hio!
Lived in Long Acre, hio!
Married a Quaker, hio!

Oh, the ladies of the town, hio!
All as soft as down, hio!
In their best gown, hio!

Oh, haughty cocks, hio!
Oh, split the blocks, hio!
And stretch her luff, hio!

There is another version called *Cheer'ly, O!*

> Oh, haul pulley, yoe!
>   *Cheer'ly, men!*
> Oh, long and strong, yoe!
>   *Cheer'ly men!*
> Oh, yoe, and with a will!
>   *Cheer'ly, men!*
>   *Cheer'ly, Cheer'ly, Cheer'ly, O!*
>
> A long haul for Widow Skinner,
> Kiss her well before dinner,
> At her, boys, and win her!
>
> A strong pull for Mrs. Bell,
> Who likes a lark right well,
> And, what's more, will never tell!
>
> Oh, haul and split the blocks,
> Oh, haul and stretch her luff,
> Young lovelies, sweat her up!

Dana offers a revealing glimpse of the morale of the American sailor of his time. It was after the cruel floggings of the sailors, Sam and John the Swede, by Captain Thompson: "In no operation can the disposition of a crew be better discovered than in getting under way. Where things are done 'with a will,' every one is like a cat aloft; sails are loosed in an instant; each one lays out his strength on his handspike, and the windlass goes briskly round with the loud cry of 'yo heave ho! Heave and pawl! Heave hearty, ho!' and the chorus of 'Cheerily, men!' cats the anchor. But with us, at this time, it was all dragging work. No one went aloft beyond his ordinary gait, and the chain came slowly in over the windlass. The mate, between the knight-heads, exhausted all his official rhetoric in calls of 'Heave with a will!' 'Heave hearty, men! heave hearty!' 'Heave, and raise the dead!' 'Heave, and away!' etc., etc., but it would not do. Nobody broke his back or his handspike by his efforts. And when the cat-tackle-fall was strung along, and all hands, cook, steward and all, laid hold to cat the anchor, instead of the lively song of 'Cheerily, men!' in which all hands join the chorus, we pulled a long, heavy, silent pull, and, as sailors say a song is as good as ten men, the anchor came to the cat-head pretty slowly. Give us 'Cheerily!' said the mate; but there was no 'cheerily' for us and we did without it."

'TWAS A LONG TIME AGO

The Black Ball Songs

THERE ARE enough versions of this justly famous old chantey
to fill a volume. It would seem to be the oldest American chantey,
dating from the earliest days of the Black Ball Line. For the purpose of this work three versions are selected and divided, quite
arbitrarily, as follows: the Original, known as The Black Ball
Line, the Liverpool, and the Shore versions. That it was originally
a long-drag chantey seems certain, but with the addition of the
first two verses it became a comeallye, a sort of chantey-ballad
used for many purposes, and as such it is sung today. The chantey
proper began at verse three.

The Black Ball Line

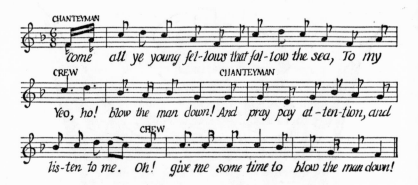

Come all ye young fellows that follow the sea,
   To my yeo, ho! blow the man down.
And pray pay attention and listen to me.
   Oh, give me some time to blow the man down!

I'm a deep water sailor just in from Hong Kong,
If you'll give me some whiskey I'll sing you my song.

'Twas on a Black Baller I first served my time,
And on that Black Baller I wasted my prime.

'Tis when a Black Baller's preparin' for sea,
You'd split your sides laughing at the sights you see.

With the tinkers and tailors and sogers and all,
That ship for prime seamen on board a Black Ball.

'Tis when a Black Baller is clear of the land,
Our boatswain then gives us the word of command.

"Lay aft," is the cry, "to the break of the poop!
Or I'll help you along with the toe of my boot!"

'Tis larboard and starboard on the deck you will sprawl,
For "Kicking Jack" Williams commands that Black Ball.

Pay attention to orders, now you one and all,
For right there above you flies the Black Ball.

'Tis when a Black Baller comes back to her dock,
To my yeo, ho! blow the man down!
The lads and the lasses to the pierhead do flock.
Oh, give me some time to blow the man down!

Robert Greenhalgh Albion in his splendid *Square Riggers on Schedule* states that the only Captain Williams in the Black Ball service was John Williams, of the *Pacific,* and that he did not have the reputation of a bucko. Captain John Williams was lost at sea in the wreck of the *Albion,* off Old Head, Kinsdale, Ireland, April 5, 1822. Many years later another Captain John H. Williams commanded the *Gladiator* and the *American Congress* in the Red Swallowtail Line to London. Captain A. H. Clark tells of a third, Captain John E. Williams, of Mystic, Connecticut, who commanded the California clipper, *Andrew Jackson.*

Some day a daring singer is going to change blow to knock and it won't hurt the old song any. No one has ever explained why the old sailorman was so happy in the contemplation of knocking people down, why he had to have time, or why he continues after all these years to sing about it. The following is the Liverpool version.

Blow the Man Down, I

Oh, blow the man down, boys, blow the man down,
Way ay, blow the man down!
Oh, blow the man down in Liverpool town,
Give me some time to blow the man down!

As I was walking down Paradise Street,
A brass-bound policeman I happened to meet.

Says he, "You're a Black Baller by the cut of your hair,
I know you're a Black Baller by the clothes that you wear."

"Oh, policeman, policeman, you do me great wrong,
I'm a *Flying Fish* sailor just in from Hong Kong."

They gave me three months in Walton Gaol,
 Way ay, blow the man down!
For booting and kicking and blowing him down,
 Give me some time to blow the man down!

Blow the Man Down, II

As I was walking down Paradise Street,
 Way, ay,—blow the man down!
A saucy young clipper I happened to meet,
 Give me some time to blow the man down!

Her flag was three colors, her masts they were low,
She was round in the counter and bluff in the bow.

I dipped her my ensign, a signal she knew,
For she backed round her mainyards and hove herself to.

I hailed her in English, she answered "Aye, aye!"
She was from the Blue Water and bound for Tiger Bay.

I passed her my hawser and took her in tow,
And yardarm to yardarm away we did go.

We tossed along gaily, both friskly and fleet,
 Way ay, blow the man down!
Till she dropped her bow anchor, 'twas in Avon Street,
 Give me some time to blow the man down!

In a waterside saloon this can be carried much farther without
becoming any more interesting. There is another shore version
entitled "While Strolling through Norfolk," the only one in
which the traditional chorus lines are abandoned for the following:

Singing fal de eye idol, sing fal de eye idol,
Sing fal de eye idol, sing fal de eye de aye!

THE SAILORS RETURN

KEEP ON IT

Lowlands

THE WRITER first heard this capstan chantey in a dense fog off Quarantine: our ship had come up in the night and anchored in the Narrows awaiting the clearing. Tumbling on deck at dawn, unable to see our hands before our faces, let alone the always welcome green hills of Staten Island, we tried to find our position with our ears. All we could distinguish was the clanking of an anchor chain on our starboard, the noises usual in an iron ship, more sonorous because of the fog, and then a doleful voice with a Cockney accent singing the song as a ballad. It was the perfect setting for a dirge.

I dreamed my love came in my sleep,
   Lowlands, Lowlands, away, my John.
His eyes were wet as he did weep,
   My Lowlands, away!

I shall never kiss you again, he said,
   Lowlands, Lowlands, away, my John!
For I am drowned in the Lowland seas.
   My Lowlands, away!

No other man shall think me fair,
   Lowlands, Lowlands, away, my John!
My love lies drowned in the windy Lowlands,
   My Lowlands, away!

That the chantey derives from an old Scottish coronach, "The Lawlands o' Holland," seems evident, and English Jack handled it with more or less reverence.

The Lawlands o' Holland

The love that I hae chosen,
   I'll therewith be content;
The saut sea sall be frozen
   Before that I repent.
Repent it sall I never
   Until the day I dee;
But the Lawlands o' Holland
   Hae twinn'd * my love and me.

My love he built a bonny ship,
   And set her to the main,
Wi' twenty-four brave mariners
   To sail her out and hame.
But the weary wind began to rise,
   The sea began to rout,
And my love and his bonny ship
   Turned withershins † about.

There sall nae mantle cross my back,
   Nor kaim gae in my hair,
Neither sall coal nor candle light
   Shine in my bower mair;
Nor sall I choose anither love
   Until the day I dee,
Sin' the Lawlands o' Holland
   Hae twinn'd my love and me.

Noo haud your tongue, my daughter dear,
   Be still, and bide content;
There's ither lads in Galloway;
   Ye needna sair lament.

* twinn'd: parted
† withershins: counterclockwise, the way witches dance, possibly the ship
turned turtle.

O, there is nane in Galloway,
There's nane at a' for me.
I never lo'ed a lad but ane,
And he's drown'd in the sea.

Lowlands suffered a sea change in crossing the Atlantic. The American sailor cared little enough for dirges: laments, yes, and gripes. In many versions he complained bitterly that he received but a dollar a day while the Negro roustabouts with whom he worked were paid a dollar and a half a day.

Lowlands, II

Lowlands, lowlands, away, my John,
My old mother she wrote to me,
  My dollar and a half a day!
She wrote to me to come home from sea,
  Lowlands, lowlands, away, my John!
She wrote to me to come home from sea.
  My dollar and a half a day!

Lowlands, lowlands, away, my John,
Oh, were you ever in Mobile Bay?
  My dollar and a half a day!
A-screwing cotton by the day,
  Lowlands, lowlands, away, my John!
A-screwing cotton by the day,
  My dollar and a half a day!

Lowlands, lowlands, away, my John,
A dollar a day is a Hoosier's pay,
  My dollar and a half a day!
Yes, a dollar a day is a Hoosier's pay,
  Lowlands, lowlands, away, my John!

Yes, a dollar a day is a Hoosier's pay.
My dollar and a half a day!

Lowlands, III

I wish I were in the Dutchman's Hall,
  Lowlands, lowlands, hurrah, my boys!
A-drinking luck to the old Black Ball.
  My dollar and a half a day!

A Long Time Ago

Long-drag Chantey

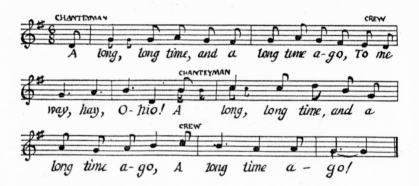

A long, long time, and a long time ago,
To me way, hay, o-hio!
A long, long time, and a long time ago,
A long time ago!

A smart Yankee packet lay out in the bay,
A-waiting for a fair wind to get under way,

With all her poor sailors all sick and all sad,
For they'd drunk all their whiskey, no more could be had,

She was waiting for a fair wind to get under way,
To me way, hay, o-hio!
If she hasn't had a fair wind she's lying there still.
A long time ago!

A more recent version using the same melody.

Around Cape Horn

Around Cape Horn we've got to go,
  To me way, hay, o-hio!
Around Cape Horn to Call-eao,
  A long time ago!

'Round Cape Horn where the stiff winds blow,
'Round Cape Horn where there's sleet and snow.

I wish to God I'd never been born
  To me way, hay, o-hio!
To drag my carcass around Cape Horn.
  A long time ago!

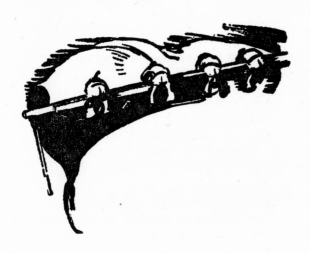

Reuben Ranzo

THIS LONG-DRAG chantey starts off on a note of disarming sympathy for poor Reuben, supposedly one Reuben Lorenzo, who was anything but a sailor. But that sympathy is short-lived and the chantey becomes a caustic comment on all foremasthands who curry favor with the captain to gain a place on the quarterdeck. Captain Whall insists he never heard any improvisations, but there are so many versions we must credit his lack of information traceable to the fact he never served on an American vessel.

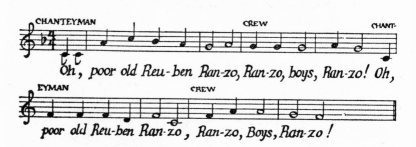

Oh, poor old Reu-ben Ran-zo, Ran-zo, boys, Ran-zo! Oh, poor old Reu-ben Ran-zo, Ran-zo, Boys, Ran-zo!

Oh, poor old Reuben Ranzo,
   Ranzo, boys, Ranzo!
Oh, pity poor Reuben Ranzo,
   Ranzo, boys, Ranzo!

Oh, Ranzo was no sai-lor,
He shipped aboard a wha-ler.

Oh, Ranzo was no beau-ty,
He could not do his du-ty.

So, they gave him nine and thir-ty,
Yes, lashes nine and thir-ty.

KEEP ON

THE ANCHOR

THE
MAID OF
AMSTERDAM

Oh, cap'n being a good man,
He took him to the cab-an.

He gave him wine and wa-ter,
Rube kissed the cap'n's daugh-ter.

He taught him navi-gashun,
To fit him for his stay-shun.

Now, Ranzo, he's a sai-lor,
Chief mate of that wha-ler.

He married the cap'n's daugh-ter,
  Ranzo, boys, Ranzo!
And sails no more upon the wa-ter.
  Ranzo, boys, Ranzo!

In some instances the final verse goes:

Now, he's cap'n of a Black Ball li-ner,
  Ranzo, boys, Ranzo!
And nothing could be fi-ner.
  Ranzo, boys, Ranzo!

Hanging Johnny

Long-drag Chantey

They call me Hanging Johnny,
A-way-i-oh!
They say I hang for money,
So hang, boys, hang!

First I hung my mother,
Then I hung my brother.

I'll hang you all together,
A-way-i-oh!
We'll hang for better weather,
So hang, boys, hang!

A good chanteyman could hang quite a lot if the task lasted long enough.

Whiskey for My Johnny

Long-drag Chantey

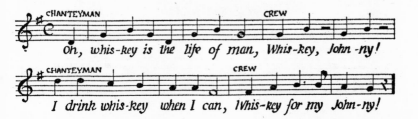

Oh, whiskey is the life of man,
  Whiskey, Johnny!
I drink whiskey when I can
  Whiskey for my Johnny!

Whiskey from an old tin can,
I'll drink whiskey when I can.

I drink it hot, I drink it cold,
I drink it new, I drink it old.

Whiskey makes me feel so sad,
Whiskey killed my poor old dad.

I thought I heard the old man say,
I'll treat my crew in a decent way.

A glass of grog for every man,
And a bottle full for the chanteyman.

Tommy's Gone to Hilo

Long-drag Chantey

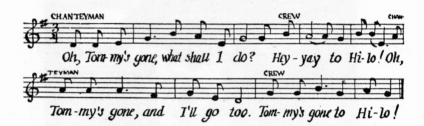

Oh, Tom-my's gone, what shall I do? Hey-yay to Hi-lo! Oh, Tom-my's gone, and I'll go too. Tom-my's gone to Hi-lo!

Oh, Tommy's gone, what shall I do?
Hey-yay to Hi-lo!
Oh, Tommy's gone, and I'll go too.
Tommy's gone to Hi-lo!

Oh, I love Tom and he loves me,
He thinks of me when out to sea.

Oh, away around to Callao,
The Spanish gels he'll see, I know.

Oh, Tommy's gone for evermore,
Hey-yay to Hi-lo!
I'll never see my Tom no more.
Tommy's gone to Hi-lo!

Hilo is Ilo, the southernmost port in Peru. For long periods Chilean ports were closed to foreign vessels and skippers coming up the West Coast from the Cape Horn passage put in at Ilo for water. It was also a guano port and something of a message center for whalers.

JOSIAH PERKINS CRESSY
MASTER
SHIP FLYING CLOUD

Blow, Bullies, Blow

Long-drag Chantey

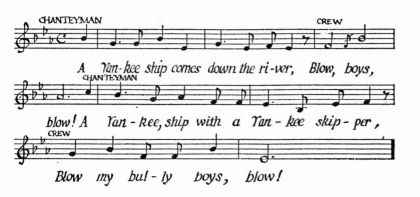

CHANTEYMAN: A Yan-kee ship comes down the ri-ver, CREW: Blow, boys, blow! CHANTEYMAN: A Yan-kee, ship with a Yan-kee skip-per, CREW: Blow my bul-ly boys, blow!

A Yankee ship comes down the river,
  Blow, boys, blow!
A Yankee ship with a Yankee skipper,
  Blow, my bully boys, blow!

How do you know she's a Yankee clipper;
Because her masts and yards shine like silver.

Who do you think is captain of her?
Old Holy Joe, the darky lover.

What do you think she's got for cargo?
Why, "black sheep" that have run the embargo.

What do you think they'll have for dinner?
Why, monkeys' tails and bullocks' liver.

Oh, blow today and blow tomorrow,
   Blow, boys, blow!
Oh, blow me down to the Congo River,
   Blow, my bully boys, blow!

    A maverick verse that still has some currency in New England is:

Oh, Captain Hall was a Boston slaver,
   Blow, boys, blow!
He traded in niggers and loved his Maker,
   Blow, my bully boys, blow!

Early in the Morning

THIS SONG, capstan chantey or walkaway chorus, is heard more often ashore than afloat. The writer first heard it used as a quick-time effect in a New York National Guard drill, and it was very effective for use in training recruits, save that the stomping that went with it was not in the best military tradition. More recently it was heard used as a conga dance tune.

> Way, hay, there she rises,
> Way, hay, there she rises,
> Way, hay, there she rises,
>   Early in the morning!
> What will we do with a drunken sailor?
> What will we do with a drunken sailor?
> What will we do with a drunken sailor?
>   Early in the morning!

> Way, hay, there she rises,
> Way, hay, there she rises,
> Way, hay, there she rises,
>   Early in the morning!
> Put him in the longboat and make him bale her,
> Put him in the longboat and make him bale her,
> Put him in the longboat and make him bale her,
>   Early in the morning!

Way, hay, there she rises,
Way, hay, there she rises,
Way, hay, there she rises,
Early in the morning!
What will we do with a drunken soldier?
What will we do with a drunken soldier?
What will we do with a drunken soldier?
Early in the morning!

Way, hay, there she rises,
Way, hay, there she rises,
Way, hay, there she rises,
Early in the morning!
Put him in the guardroom till he gets sober,
Put him in the guardroom till he gets sober,
Put him in the guardroom till he gets sober,
Early in the morning!

Stormalong

OLD STORMALONG is the only heroic character in the folklore of the sea: he was born, like the great clipper ships, in the imaginations of men. There is a legend, told in prose, of the time he was quartermaster of the *Courser*, the world's largest clipper. Stormy was taking his vessel from the North Sea through the English Channel, which was just six inches narrower than the *Courser's* beam. He suggested that if the captain sent all hands over to plaster the ship's side with soap he thought he could ease her through. It was a tight passage but the ship made it, the Dover cliffs scraping all the soap off the starboard side. Ever since, the cliffs at that point have been pure white and recent observers say the waves there are still foamy from the *Courser's* soap.

This version was used as a capstan chantey.

Oh, Stormy's gone, that good old man,
 To my way hay, Stormalong, John!
Oh, poor old Stormy's dead and gone,
 To my aye, aye, aye, aye, Mister Stormalong!

We dug his grave with a silver spade,
His shroud of the finest silk was made.

We lowered him with a silver chain,
Our eyes all dim with more than rain.

An able sailor, bold and true,
A good old bosun to his crew.

He's moored at last, and furled his sail,
No danger now from wreck or gale.

I wish I was old Stormy's son,
I'd build me a ship of a thousand ton.

I'd fill her up with New England rum,
And all my shellbacks they would have some.

I'd sail this wide world 'round and 'round,
With plenty of money I would be found.

Old Stormy's dead and gone to rest,
   To my way hay, Stormalong, John!
Of all the sailors he was the best,
   To my aye, aye, aye, aye, Mister Stormalong!

Shenandoah

THIS CAPSTAN chantey has, without question, the loveliest
melody of all sailor songs. It has, too, the greatest number of
variants, many of them muddled and most of them on the side of
gibberish. In some, Shenandoah is an Indian chief, a bright mulatto,
a savage maiden, and she has been mistaken for Sally Brown. In
Virginia, where there is a river by the name, Shenandoah means
"daughter of the stars," which gives a clue to the sailors' loving
the daughter: how the wide Missouri got in is a mystery.

The old sailors sang it "Shannadore" and "Mizzouray."

Oh, Shenandoah, I love your daughter,
A-way, my rol-ling ri-ver!
I'll take her 'cross yon rolling water.
Ah, hah! We're bound away,
'Cross the wide Missouri!

Oh, Shenandoah, I love your Nancy,
Oh, Shenandoah, she took my fancy.

Oh, Shenandoah, I long to hear you,
'Cross that wide and rol-ling riv-er.

Oh, Shenandoah, I'll ne'er forget you,
Away, my rol-ling ri-ver!
Till the day I die, I'll love you ever.
Ah, hah! We're bound away,
'Cross the wide Missouri!

Paddy Get Back

A CAPSTAN chantey, called by Captain Bone, "The Liverpool Song," that seems to be of a recent and questionable birth, possibly one sired by sailors who went from sail to steam and back again without heartbreak. The fact that the term chantey is used within the song and firemen mentioned seems to warrant this conclusion. It can be recalled that the Panama Canal was not opened to general traffic until 1914 and up to that time even steamships had to double Cape Horn to make the West Coast ports.

The air and words given here are from a recording in the Archive of American Folksong in the Library of Congress.

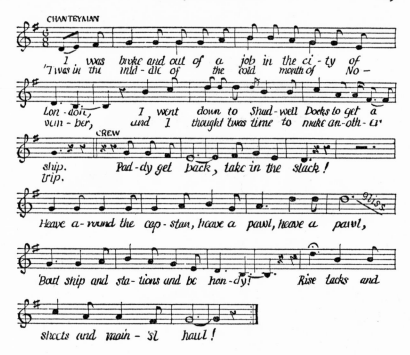

I was broke and out of a job in the city of London,
I went down to Shadwell Docks to get a ship.

Paddy get back, take in the slack!
Heave away the capstan, heave a pawl! heave a pawl!
'Bout ship and stations and be handy,
Rise tacks and sheets and mains'l haul!

There was a Yankee ship a-laying in the basin,
And they told me she was going to New York.

If I ever lay my hands on that shipping-master,
I'll murder him if it's the last thing that I do.

When the pilot left the ship 'way down the Channel,
Oh, the captain told us we were going around Cape Horn.

The mate and the second mate belonged in Boston,
And the captain hailed from Bangor down in Maine.

The three of them were rough-and-tumble fighters,
When not fighting amongst themselves they turned on us.

They called us out one night to reef the topsails,
Now belaying pins were flying around the deck.

And we came on deck and went to set the topsails,
Not a man in the bunch could sing a song.

We are tinkers, we are tailors, and the fireman also cooks,
And they couldn't sing a chantey unless they had the books.

Wasn't that a bunch of hoodlums,
For to take a ship around Cape Horn?

Paddy get back, take in the slack!
Heave away the capstan, heave a pawl! heave a pawl!
'Bout ship and stations and be handy,
Rise tacks and sheets and mains'l haul!

Across the Western Ocean

THERE IS GOOD reason to believe that there was an earlier version of this westward bound capstan chantey. The Irish coming to America in droves left their impress on the songs, legends, and salty speech of the sailorman. The "Amelia" mentioned may have been the name of a vessel; there were two packets by that name but both were in the coastal service, there was a brig, *Amelia Strong*, and an English bark, *Amelia Packet*. It may have been a corruption of O'Malley or, quite likely, it was a girl by that name.

The Irish Army referred to in the second verse was probably the hordes leaving starving Ireland, though there was a sort of Irish-Army-in-Exile on the Continent (see "The Girl I Left behind Me"). Yet the term may have been ironic: sailors liked to refer to a large and unwieldy barge that had to be towed as an Irish man-of-war, and an Irish hurricane was rain and fog on a calm sea. An Irish pennant was any rope or sail that had broken loose and was blowing free in the wind.

On one of the packet ships, a storm came up and a devout Irishman assured the sailors that the waves were caused by the writhings of the snakes and serpents that St. Patrick had driven out of Ireland.

Oh, the times are hard and the wages low,
  Amelia, where you bound to?
The Rocky Mountains is my home,
  Across the Western Ocean.

The land of promise there you'll see,
  Amelia, where you bound to?
I'm bound across that Western sea,
  To join the Irish army.

To Liverpool I'll take my way,
  Amelia, where you bound to?
To Liverpool that Yankee school,
  Across the Western Ocean.

There's Liverpool Pat with his tarpaulin hat,
  Amelia, where you bound to?
And Yankee John, the packet rat.
  Across the Western Ocean.

Beware these packet ships, I say,
  Amelia, where you bound to?
They steal your stores and clothes away,
  Across the Western Ocean.

We're All Bound to Go

THIS CAPSTAN chantey also dates from the great Irish emigration to America in the Forties and Fifties. Miss Joanna Colcord identifies William Tapscott as a Liverpool shipping agent. The *Henry Clay* was a famous packet, Ezra Nye, master, built in New York in 1845 for the Swallowtail Line to Liverpool. In 1846 she was wrecked on the New Jersey Monmouth coast with a loss of several lives but was brought off and within a few months put back on the old run. On September 5, 1849, she burned at her South Street pier. Her charred hulk was sold to the Collins Dramatic Line, which rebuilt and restored her to the Liverpool service. At the end of the Civil War she was operating as a freight packet.

> Oh, as I walked down the Landing Stage,
> All on a Summer's morn,
> *Heave away, my Johnny, heave away!*
> It's there I spied an Irish girl
> A-looking all forlorn.
> *And away, my Johnnie boys,*
> *We're all bound to go!*

"Oh, good morning, Mr. Tapscott,"
"Good morning, my girl," says he,
  Heave away, my Johnny, heave away!
"Have you got a packet ship
To carry me across the sea?"
  And away, my Johnnie boys,
  We're all bound to go!

"Oh, yes, I have a clipper ship,
She's called the *Henry Clay*,"
  Heave away, my Johnny, heave away!
"She sails today for Boston Bay,
She sails away at break of day."
  And away, my Johnnie boys,
  We're all bound to go!

"Oh, will you take me to Boston Bay,
When she sails away at break of day?"
  Heave away, my Johnny, heave away!
"I want to marry a Yankee boy,
And I'll cross the sea no more."
  And away, my Johnnie boys,
  We're all bound to go!

KEEP ON

Paddy Works on the Railway

THIS CAPSTAN chantey shows that Jack could imitate the counting songs of the children. Many of the Irish emigrants went directly from the packets to the railway construction camps, and when Sailor Jack heard the wages Irish Paddy would get he followed along, at least for the cold, wintry months. Returning to the sea with the first breath of Spring, he brought the song back with him, half identifying himself with the Irish workers. The following version, placed in the Forties, is a fabrication made up of snatches in which the dates jump from the Forties to the Seventies and back again.

Oh, in eighteen hundred and forty-one,
My corduroy breeches I put on,
My time was nearly done.
    To work upon the railway, the railway,
    I'm weary of the railway,
    Oh, poor Paddy works on the railway.

Oh, in eighteen hundred and forty-two,
My corduroy breeches then were new,
I did not know what I should do.

Oh, in eighteen hundred and forty-three,
I sailed away across the sea,
I sailed away to Amerikee.

Oh, in eighteen hundred and forty-four,
I landed on the Columbia shore,
I had a pick-ax and nothing more.

Oh, in eighteen hundred and forty-five,
When Dan O'Connelly was still alive,
I worked in a railway hive.

Oh, in eighteen hundred and forty-six,
I found myself in a hell of a fix;
I changed my job to toting bricks.

Oh, in eighteen hundred and forty-seven,
When Dan O'Connelly went to heaven,
Little Paddy was going on eleven.

Oh, in eighteen hundred and forty-eight,
I found myself bound for the Golden Gate,
Gold was found in the western state.

Oh, in eighteen hundred and forty-nine,
I passed my time in the Black Ball Line.
And that's the end of my monkeyshine.

> *To work upon the railway, the railway,*
> *I'm weary of the railway,*
> *Oh, poor Paddy works on the railway.*

Santa Anna
or The Plains of Mexico

THIS IS a curious capstan chantey that must go unexplained. In some versions the roles of Santa Anna and General Taylor are reversed and it is the American who ran away. Jack, like a lot of other people, just didn't give a damn for historical fact. It is admitted that history is what happened and folklore is what the people think happened. This is folklore.

Oh, Santa Anna fought for fame,
  Hooray, Santa Anna!
He fought for fame and gained his name,
  Along the plains of Mexico!

General Taylor gained the day,
  Hooray, Santa Anna!
And Santa Anna ran away,
  Along the plains of Mexico!

Maid of Amsterdam (A-Roving)

BACK IN 1608 Thomas Heywood, an English dramatist, wrote *The Rape of Lucrece* and in the production of the play this song was introduced. Heywood was something of a play-carpenter, he claimed to have written or "had a main finger in" no less than two hundred and twenty plays. No one can say whether Tom lifted the song from Jack or whether the reverse is true. What is known is that for over three hundred years the Maid has been a-roving and spreading ru-in across land and sea.

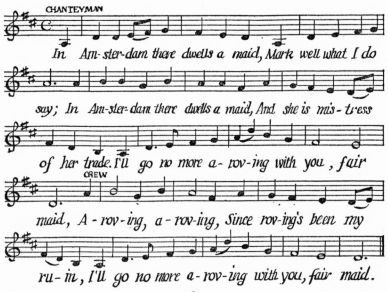

CHANTEYMAN

In Am-ster-dam there dwells a maid, Mark well what I do say; In Am-ster-dam there dwells a maid, And she is mis-tress of her trade. I'll go no more a-rov-ing with you, fair maid,

CREW

A-rov-ing, a-rov-ing, Since rov-ing's been my ru-in, I'll go no more a-rov-ing with you, fair maid.

In Amsterdam there dwells a maid,
  Mark well what I do say;
In Amsterdam there dwells a maid,
  And she is mistress of her trade.

> *I'll go no more a-roving*
> *With you, fair maid,*
> *A-roving, a-roving,*
> *Since roving's been my ru-in,*
> *I'll go no more a-roving*
> *With you, fair maid!*

Her eyes are blue, her cheeks are red,
  Mark well what I do say;
Her eyes are blue, her cheeks are red,
  A wealth of hair is on her head.

I put my arm around her waist,
  Mark well what I do say;
I put my arm around her waist,
  Says she, "Young man, you're in some haste."

I took that girl upon my knee,
  Mark well what I do say,
I took that girl upon my knee,
  Says she, "Young man, you're rather free."

She swore that she'd be true to me,
  Mark well what I do say;
She swore that she'd be true to me,
  But spent my money both fast and **free.**

> *I'll go no more a-roving*
> *With you, fair maid,*
> *A-roving, a-roving,*
> *Since roving's been my ru-in,*
> *I'll go no more a-roving*
> *With you, fair maid!*

The Banks of the Sacramento

A Capstan chantey from the California clippers

CHANTEYMAN

Sing and heave, and heave and sing, To me hoo-dah! To my

CHANTEYMAN   CREW

hoo-dah.   Heave and make the hand-spikes spring. To me hoo-dah, hoo-dah-

day! And it's blow, boys, blow, For Cal-i-for-ni-o. For there's

plen-ty of gold, So I've been told, On the banks of the Sa-cra-men-to.

Sing and heave, and heave and sing,
To me hoodah! To my hoodah!
Heave and make the handspikes spring,
To me hoodah, hoodah, day!

And it's blow, boys, blow,
For Californi-o!
For there's plenty of gold,
So I've been told,
On the banks of the Sacramento!

From Limehouse Docks to Sydney Heads,
To me hoodah! To my hoodah!
Was never more than seventy days.
To me hoodah, hoodah, day!

We cracked it on, on a big skiute,
To me hoodah! To my hoodah!
And the old man felt like a swell galoot.
To me hoodah, hoodah, day!

And it's blow, boys, blow,
For Californi-o!
For there's plenty of gold,
So I've been told,
On the banks of the Sacramento!

Cape Cod Girls

THIS DITTY, sometimes bound for Australia, seems to be unknown to all active and retired mariners on Cape Cod. Yet every woman and child knows it and many have added verses of their own.

Cape Cod girls they have no combs,
Heave away! Heave away!
They comb their hair with codfish bones,
We're bound for Californiay!

Heave away, my bully, bully boys,
Heave away, and don't you make a noise.

Cape Cod boys they have no sleds,
They slide down dunes on codfish heads.

Cape Cod doctors they have no pills
They give their patients codfish gills.

Cape Cod cats they have no tails,
Heave away! Heave away!
They lost them all in sou'east gales.
We're bound for Californiay!

Good-bye, Fare You Well

THIS AND the two following homeward bound chanteys were used at the capstan or windlass. All tell their own stories, all were sung with a spirit of exultation.

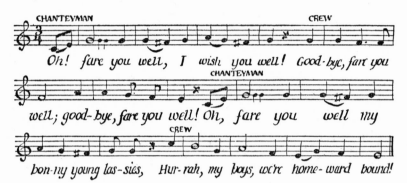

Oh, fare you well, I wish you well!
  Good-bye, fare you well; good-bye, fare you well!
Oh, fare you well, my bonny young lassies,
  Hurrah, my boys, we're homeward bound!

The billows roll, the breezes blow,
To us they're calling: sheet home and go!

We're homeward bound, and I hear the sound,
So heave on the caps'n and make it spin round.

Our anchor's aweigh and our sails they are set,
And the girls we are leaving we leave with regret.

She's a flash clipper packet and bound for to go,
  Good-bye, fare you well; good-bye, fare you well!
With the girls on her towrope she cannot say no.
  Hurrah, my boys, we're homeward bound!

85

Time to Leave Her

Oh, the work was hard and the wages low,
 Leave her, Johnny, leave her!
We'll pack our bags and go below,
 It's time for us to leave her!

The work was hard, the voyage was long,
The seas were high, the gales were strong.

The food was bad and the ship was slow,
But now ashore again we'll go.

86

It was growl you may but go you must,
It mattered not whether you're last or first.

I thought I heard the old man say,
"Just one more pull and then belay."

The sails are furled, our work is done,
 Leave her, Johnny, leave her!
And now on shore we'll have our fun.
 It's time for us to leave her!

Capstan chantey, often used, with a slight change of pace, as a pumping song.

One Day More

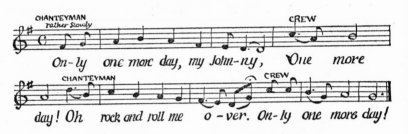

On-ly one more day, my John-ny, One more day! Oh rock and roll me o-ver. On-ly one more day!

Only one more day, my Johnny,
One more day!
Oh, rock and roll me over.
Only one more day!

Don't you hear the old man calling,
Can't you hear the pilot bawling.

Can't you hear those gals a-calling
Can't you hear the capstan pawling.

Put on your long-tailed blue, my Johnny,
For your pay is nearly due.

Only one more day, my Johnny,
One more day!
Oh, rock and roll me over.
Only one more day!

Forecastle Songs

The High Barbaree

CHARLES DIBDIN, a British editor and song writer, 1745–1814, is said to have written above twelve hundred songs, most of them for use by the Royal Navy. Among those that are still popular are "The High Barbaree," "Tom Bowline," and "Ben Backstay." Dibdin's great influence may be estimated from the fact that in 1803 the British government engaged him to write a series of songs designed "to keep alive the national feelings against the French."

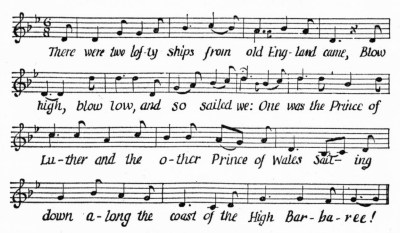

There were two lofty ships from old England came,
Blow high, blow low, and so sailed we:
One was the *Prince of Luther* and the other *Prince of Wales*,
Sailing down along the coast of the High Barbaree!

"Aloft there, aloft!" our jolly boatswain cries
　Blow high, blow low, and so sailed we:
"Look ahead, look astern, look aweather and alee,
　　Look along down the coast of the High Barbaree!"

"There's nought upon our stern, there's nought upon our lee,"
　Blow high, blow low, and so sailed we:
"But there's a lofty ship to windward, she's sailing fast and free,
　　Sailing down along the coast of the High Barbaree!"

"Oh, hail her, oh, hail her!" our gallant captain cried,
　Blow high, blow low, and so sailed we:
"Are you a man-of-war or a Yankee privateer?" asked he,
　　"Cruising down along the coast of the High Barbaree!"

"Oh, I am not a man-of-war nor privateer," said she,
　Blow high, blow low, and so sailed we:
"But I am a deep-sea pirate, a-looking for my fee."
　　Cruising down along the coast of the High Barbaree!

"If you are a jolly pirate, we'd have you come this way!"
　Blow high, blow low, and so sailed we:
"Bring out your quarter guns, we'll show these pirates play,"
　　Cruising down along the coast of the High Barbaree!

'Twas broadside to broadside a long time we lay,
　Blow high, blow low, and so sailed we:
Until the *Prince of Luther* shot the pirate's masts away,
　　Cruising down along the coast of the High Barbaree!

"Oh, quarter, Oh, quarter," those pirates then did cry,
　Blow high, blow low, and so sailed we:
But the quarter that we gave them—we sank them in the sea,
　　Cruising down along the coast of the High Barbaree!

FLYING CLOUD

MAN OF WAR AND A CUTTER

'Way Down in Cuba

A WIDE SEARCH for this elusive Mississippi River song brought only the following:

> I've got a sister nine feet tall,
> *'Way down in Cuba!*
> Sleeps in the kitchen with her feet in the hall.
> *'Way down in Cuba!*
>
> I've got a girl friend, name is Jane,
> *'Way down in Cuba!*
> You can guess where she gives me a pain.
> *'Way down in Cuba!*

KEEP ON

Tom Bowline

Here, a sheer hulk lies poor Tom Bow-line, The dar-ling of our crew; No more he'll hear the tem-pest howl-ing, For death has broach'd him to. His form was of the man-liest beau-ty, His heart was kind and soft; Faith-ful be-low, he did his du-ty, And now he's gone a-loft. And now he's gone a-loft.

Here, a sheer hulk, lies poor Tom Bowline,
   The darling of our crew;
No more he'll hear the tempest howling,
   For death has broach'd him to.
His form was of the manliest beauty,
   His heart was kind and soft;
Faithful below, he did his duty,
   And now he's gone aloft.

Tom never from his word departed,
   His virtues were so rare,
His friends were many, and true-hearted,
   His Poll was kind and fair:
And then he'd sing so blithe and jolly,
   Ah, many's the time and oft!
But mirth is turned to melancholy,
   For Tom is gone aloft.

Yet shall poor Tom find pleasant weather,
   When He, who all commands,
Shall give, to call life's crew together,
   The word to pipe all hands.
Thus Death, who kings and tars dispatches,
   In vain Tom's life has doff'd,
For, though his body's under hatches,
   His soul has gone aloft.

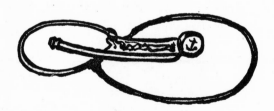

Ben Backstay

Ben Backstay was our boatswain,
A very merry boy,
For no one half so merrily
Could pipe all hands ahoy,
And when unto his summons
We did not well attend,
No lad than he more merrily,
Could handle the rope's end.

Singing chip chow, cherry chow,
Fol de riddle ido.
Singing chip chow, cherry chow,
Fol de riddle ido.

While sailing once, our captain,
Who was a jolly dog,
Served out to all the company,
A double share of grog.

BEN BACKSTAY

PRETTY POL

Ben Backstay he got tipsy,
All to his heart's content,
And he being half seas over,
Why overboard he went.

A shark was on the larboard bow,
Sharks don't on manners stand,
But grapple all they come near,
Just like your sharks on land.
We heaved Ben out some tackling
Of saving him some hope's,
But the shark had bit his head off,
So he couldn't see the ropes.

Without his head his ghost appeared
All on the briny lake;
He piped all hands ahoy and cried:
"Lads, warning by me take;
By drinking grog I lost my life,
So, lest my fate you meet,
Why, never mix your liquors, lads,
But always take them neat."

A HEART OF OAK

The *Dreadnought*

THE *Dreadnought* was a clipper, 1413 tons, built in 1853 by
New York owners at Newburyport, Massachusetts, for Captain
Samuel Samuels, who superintended her construction. She made
some remarkably fast passages between New York and Liverpool
under the flag of the Red Cross Line. Captain Clark states that
Captain Samuels believed in the use of an enterprising press agent,
and as a result the *Dreadnought* became the best publicized of all
the clippers. It is within reason to believe the publicist may have
had a hand in the writing of the ballad. The ship went down
while doubling Cape Horn in 1869.

I first heard the song during the years of the first World War,
and the three who sang it ended each verse with the line, "She's

the Liverpool packet, Oh, Lord, let her go!" as a chorus which was
shouted rather than sung.

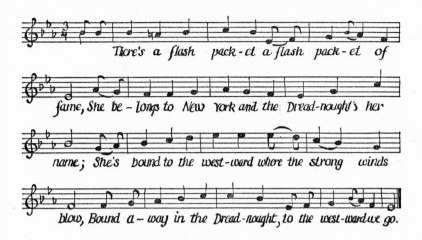

There's a flash packet, a flash packet of fame,
She belongs to New York and the *Dreadnought's* her name;
She's bound to the westward where the strong winds blow,
Bound away in the *Dreadnought*, to the westward we go.

The time for her sailing is now drawing nigh,
Farewell, pretty May, I must bid you good-bye,
Farewell to old England and all we hold dear,
Bound away in the *Dreadnought*, to the westward we'll steer.

Oh, the *Dreadnought* is pulling out of Waterloo Dock,
Where the boys and the girls to the pierheads do flock;
They will give us three cheers while their tears do flow,
Saying, "God bless the *Dreadnought*, where'er she may go!"

Oh, the *Dreadnought* is waiting in the Mersey so free,
Waiting for the *Independence* to tow her to sea;
For around that Rock Light where the Mersey does flow,
Bound away in the *Dreadnought*, to the westward we'll go.

Oh, the *Dreadnought's* a-bowlin' down the wild Irish Sea,
Where the passengers are merry, their hearts full of glee,
While her sailors like lions walk the decks to and fro,
She's the Liverpool packet, Oh, Lord, let her go!

Oh, the *Dreadnought's* a-sailin' the Atlantic so wide,
While the dark, heavy seas roll along her black sides,
With her sails neatly spread and the red cross to show,
She's the Liverpool packet, Oh, Lord, let her go!

Oh, the *Dreadnought's* becalmed on the banks of Newfoundland,
Where the water's so green and the bottom is sand;
Where the fish of the ocean swim round to and fro,
She's the Liverpool packet, Oh, Lord, let her go!

Oh, the *Dreadnought's* arrived in America once more,
Let's go ashore, shipmates, on the land we adore,
With wives and sweethearts so happy we'll be,
Drink a health to the *Dreadnought,* wherever she be.

Here's a health to the *Dreadnought,* to all her brave crew,
Here's a health to her captain, and her officers, too,
Talk about your flash packets, Swallowtail and Black Ball,
Then, here's to the *Dreadnought,* the packet to beat them all.

The *Bigler*

THE GREAT LAKES sailors had adventures no less renowned than those of the salt-water men. Their voyages did not have the length of the clippers, but the storms on the lakes were of sufficient ferocity to wreck ships and drown sailors.

The following version is by Captain Asel Trueblood, of St. Ignace, Michigan, and is taken from a record in the Archive of American Folksong in the Library of Congress.

On the Sunday morning, just at the hour of ten,
When the tug *Mico Robert* towed the schooner *Bigler*, through
Lake Michigan.
Oh, there we made our canvas in the middle of the fleet,
And the wind hauled to the south'ard, boys, so we had to give her
sheet.

CHORUS: Watch her, catch her, jump up in her ju-baju,
Give her sheet and let her go, the lads will pull her
through.

And don't you hear her howling when the wind was
    blowing free
On our down trip to Buffalo from Milwaukee.

The wind comes down from the south, southeast; it blows both
    stiff and strong,
You'd ought to've seen that little schooner *Bigler* as she pulled out
    Lake Michigan.
Oh, far beyond her foaming bows, the fiery lights aflame,
With every stitch of canvas and her course was wing and wing.

Passing by the Proctors the wind was blowing free,
Sailing by the Beavers with the Skillaglee on our lea;
Oh, we hauled her in full and bye as close as she would lie,
And we weathered Waugoshance to enter the Straits of Macki-
    naw.

At Huron we made Presque Isle Light and then we tore away,
The wind it being fair, for the Isle of Thunder Bay.
Then the wind it shifted and the night it came on dark,
The captain kept a sharp lookout for the light at Point aux Barques.

We passed the light and kept in sight of Michigan north shore,
A-boomin' for the river as we'd often done before.
When just abreast of Port Huron Light, both anchors we let go,
And the *Sweepstake* came 'longside and took the *Bigler* in tow.

She took the seven of us in tow, all of us fore and aft,
She towed us down to Lake St. Clare and stuck us on the flat.
Then eased the *Hunter's* tow line to give us all relief,
The *Bigler* fell astern and went into a boat called the *Maple Leaf*.

And then the *Sweepstake* towed us out beyond the river light,
Lake Erie for to roam and the blustering winds to fight.
The wind being from the south'ard, it blew a pretty gale,
And we took it as it came for we could not carry sail.

We made the Eau and passed Long Point, the wind now blowing
  free,
We bowled along the Canada shore, Port Colborne on our lee.
What is that that looms ahead? We knew as we drew near,
That blazing like a star, shone the light on Buffalo Pier.

And now we're safely moored in the Buffalo Creek at last,
And under Brigg's elevator the *Bigler* is made fast.
And in some lager beer saloon we'll let the bottle pass,
For we're all happy shipmates and we like a social glass.

~ SIGNALLING FOR A PILOT ~

CHINESE PIRATES

Young Monroe at Gerry's Rock[*]

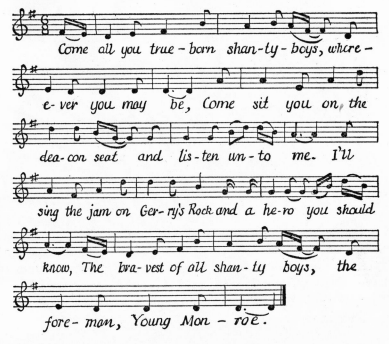

Come all you true-born shanty-boys, where-
e-ver you may be, Come sit you on the
dea-con seat and lis-ten un-to me. I'll
sing the jam on Ger-ry's Rock and a he-ro you should
know, The bra-vest of all shan-ty boys, the
fore-man, Young Mon - roe.

Come all you true-born shanty-boys, wherever you may be,
Come sit you on the deacon seat and listen unto me.
I'll sing the jam on Gerry's Rock and a hero you should know,
The bravest of all shanty-boys, the foreman, Young Monroe.

[*] From *More Pious Friends and Drunken Companions.* Copyright, 1928, by Frank Shay.

III

It was on a Sunday morning, as you will quickly hear,
Our logs were piled mountain high, we could not keep them clear.
Our foreman said: "Come, cheer up, lads, with hearts relieved of
    fear,
We'll break the jam on Gerry's Rock and for Saginaw we'll steer."

Now some of them were willing, while others they were not,
For to work on jams on Sunday they did not think we ought;
But six of our Canuck boys did volunteer to go
And break the jam on Gerry's Rock, with the foreman, Young
    Monroe.

They had not rolled off many logs when they heard his clear voice
    say:
"I'd have you lads on your guard, for the jam will soon give way."
These words were hardly spoken when the mass did break and go,
And it carried off those six brave lads, and their foreman, Young
    Monroe.

When the rest of our shanty-boys, the sad news came to hear,
In search of their dead comrades, to the river they did steer.
Some of the mangled bodies a-floating down did go,
While crushed and bleeding near the bank was that of Young
    Monroe.

They took him from his watery grave, smoothed back his raven
    hair;
There was one fair girl among them whose sad cries rent the air;
There was one fair form among them, a maid from Saginaw town,
Whose moans and cries rose to the skies, for her true lover who'd
    gone down.

For Clara was a nice young girl, the riverman's true friend;
She with her widowed mother dear, lived near the river's bend.
The wages of her own true love the boss to her did pay,
And the shanty-boys for her made up a generous purse next day.

They buried him with sorrow deep, 'twas on the first of May;
Come all you brave shanty-boys and for your comrade pray.
Engraved upon a hemlock tree that by the grave did grow,
Was the name and date of the sad fate of the foreman, Young
    Monroe.

Fair Clara did not long survive; her heart broke with her grief,
And scarcely two months later death came to her relief.
And when this time had passed away and she was called to go,
Her last request was granted, to rest beside Young Monroe.

Come all you brave shanty-boys: I would have you call and see
Those two green mounds by the riverside, where grows the hem-
    lock tree.
The shanty-boys cleared off the wood, by the lovers there laid
    low:
'Twas handsome Clara Vernon and our foreman, Young Monroe.

I Come from Salem City

THIS IS THE argonauts' parody of Stephen Foster's "O, Susannah!" Unlike most parodies it has had a long and happy life. In hog-German it is quite amusing, beginning: Ich komm dem Salem City mit dem washbowl auf dem knee!

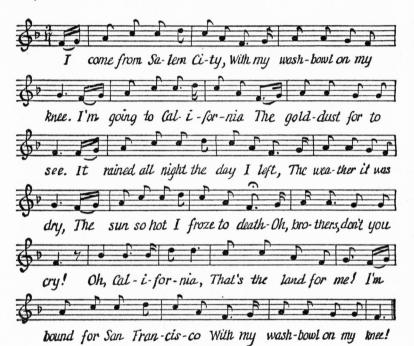

I came from Salem City,
    With my washbowl on my knee.
I'm going to California
    The gold dust for to see.
It rained all night the day I left,
    The weather it was dry,
The sun so hot I froze to death—
    Oh, brothers, don't you cry!

GOOD STUFF THIS!

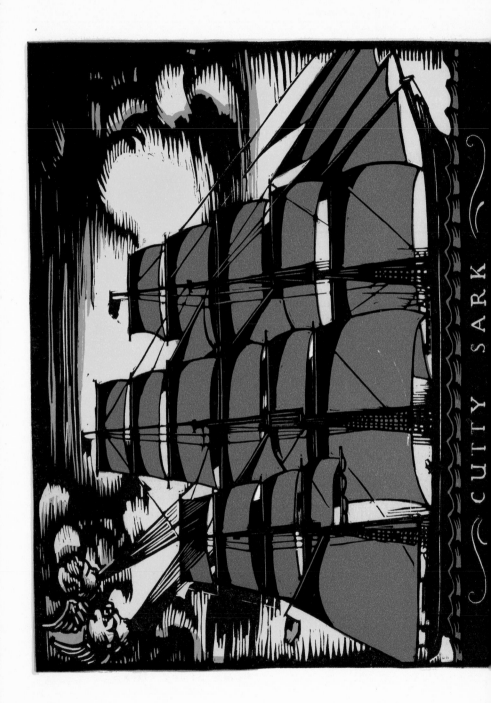
CUTTY SARK

Oh, California,
That's the land for me!
I'm bound for San Francisco
With my washbowl on my knee!

I jumped aboard the 'Liza ship
  And traveled on the sea,
And every time I thought of home
  I wished it wasn't me!
The vessel reared like any horse
  That had of oats a wealth;
I found it wouldn't throw me, so
  I thought I'd throw myself!

Chorus

I thought of all the pleasant time
  We've had together here,
I thought I ought to cry a bit,
  But couldn't find a tear.
The pilot bread was in my mouth,
  The gold dust in my eye,
And though I'm going far away,
  Dear brothers, don't you cry!

Chorus

I soon shall be in 'Frisco,
  And there I shall look around,
And when I see the gold lumps there
  I'll pick them off the ground.
I'll scrape the mountains clean, my boys,
  I'll drain the rivers dry,
A pocketful of rocks bring home—
  So, brothers, don't you cry!

A-Cruising We Will Go

Behold upon the swelling seas
  With streaming pennants gay,
Our gallant ship invites the waves,
  While glory leads the way.

    And a-cruising we will go—oho, oho, oho!
    And a-cruising we will go—oho, oho, oho!
    And a-cruising we will go—o——oho,
    And a-cruising we will go!

You beauteous maids, your smiles bestow,
  For if you prove unkind,
How can we hope to beat the foe?
  We leave our hearts behind.

    When a-cruising we will go——

See Hardy's flag once more display'd,
  Upon the deck he stands;
Britannia's glory ne'er can fade,
  Or tarnish in his hands.

    So a-cruising we will go——

Britain to herself but true,
  To France defiance hurl'd:
Give peace, America, with you,
  And war with all the world.

And a-cruising we will go—oho, oho, oho!
And a-cruising we will go—oho, oho, oho!
And a-cruising we will go—o——oho,
And a-cruising we will go!

We Be Three Poor Mariners

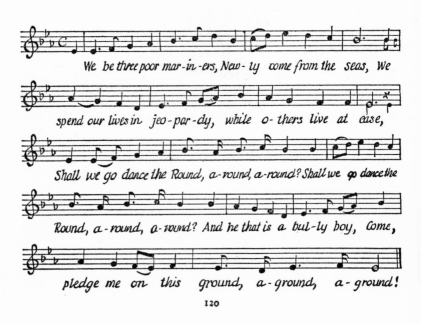

We be three poor mar-in-ers, New-ly come from the seas, We
spend our lives in jeo-par-dy, while o-thers live at ease,
Shall we go dance the Round, a-round, a-round? Shall we go dance the
Round, a-round, a-round? And he that is a bul-ly boy, Come,
pledge me on this ground, a-ground, a-ground!

We be three poor mariners, newly come from the seas,
We spend our lives in jeopardy, while others live at ease.
  Shall we go dance the Round, around, around?
  Shall we go dance the Round, around, around?
  And he that is a bully boy,
  Come, pledge me on this ground, aground, aground!

We care not for those martial men that do our states disdain;
But we care for those merchantmen that do our states maintain.
  Shall we dance this Round, around, around?
  Shall we dance this Round, around, around?
  And he that is a bully boy
  Come, pledge me on this ground, aground, aground!

The above song was first printed in 1609, and if the singer
changes dance to drink he will have an excellent bar song.

SHE BLOWS!

The Whale

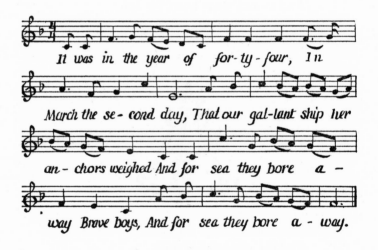

It was in the year of for-ty-four, In
March the se-cond day, That our gal-lant ship her
an-chors weighed And for sea they bore a-
way Brave boys, And for sea they bore a-way.

It was in the year of forty-four,
In March the second day,
That our gallant ship her anchors weighed
And for sea they bore away,
Brave boys,
And for sea they bore away.

And when we came to far Greenland,
  And to Greenland cold we came,
Where there's frost and snow
  And the whalefishes blow,
    Brave boys,
  And the whalefishes blow.

Our bosun went to topmast high
  With his spyglass in his hand.
"A whale! There's a whalefish," he cried,
  "And she blows at every span,
    Brave boys,
  She blows at every span."

Our captain stood on the quarter-deck,
  And a brave little man was he.
"Overhaul, overhaul, on your davit tackles fall
  And launch your boats for sea,
    Brave boys,
  And launch your boats for sea."

We struck the whale, away he went,
  And he lashed out with his tail,
And we lost the boat and five good men,
  And we never got that whale,
    Brave boys,
  And we did not get that whale.

Oh, Greenland is an awful place,
  Where the daylight's seldom seen,
Where there's frost and snow,
  And the whalefishes blow,
    Brave boys,
  And the whalefishes blow.

It is usually conceded that "The Whale" originated with the English whalers and was to some extent taken over by the Americans. In the pure English versions there is a Captain Speedicut and

many rambling and disconnected verses. In *Moby Dick* Herman
Melville has a Nantucket sailor aboard the *Pequod* sing:

> "Our captain stood upon the deck,
>   A spy-glass in his hand,
> A-viewing of those gallant whales
>   That blew at every strand.
> Oh, your tubs in your boats, my boys,
>   And by your braces stand,
> And we'll have one of those fine whales,
>   Hand, boys, over hand!

> "So be cheery, my lads! may your hearts never fail!
> While the bold harpooner is striking the whale."

In the lore of the sea Americans were impatient with most
European superstitions. They readily accepted the belief that
beginning a voyage on Friday was tempting Fate: they rejected
the idea of mermaids and that these ladies of the sea were omens of
good luck. How two omens—one good, the other bad—got into
the same verse passes understanding.

> On Friday morning we set sail,
> And our ship was not far from land,
> When there we saw a pretty maid,
> With a comb and glass in her hand,
>   Brave boys,
> With a comb and glass in her hand.

O, the captain went below,
For to light the cabin lamp;
   But he couldn't light the lamp
   Because the wick was too damn' damp.
Heave-ho, you sons of glory,
The Golden Gates are passed.

Let *go* the peak halyards,
Let *go* the peak halyards,
   My knuckles are caught in the falls.
   Let go! (shouted)

Blow, Ye Winds

*Included through the courtesy of Miss Joanna C. Colcord.**

'Tis advertised in Boston, New York and Buffalo,
Five hundred brave Americans, a-whaling for to go, singing,

CHORUS: Blow, ye winds in the morning,
And blow, ye winds, high-o!
Clear away your running gear,
And blow, ye winds, high-o!

* From *Songs of American Sailormen*, by Joanna C. Colcord. Copyright, 1938, by W. W. Norton & Company, Inc.

They send you to New Bedford, that famous whaling port,
And give you to some land-sharks to board and fit you out.

They send you to a boarding-house, there for a time to dwell;
The thieves they there are thicker than the other side of hell!

They tell you of the clipper-ships a-going in and out,
And say you'll take five hundred sperm before you're six months
    out.

It's now we're out to sea, my boys, the wind comes on to blow;
One half the watch is sick on deck, the other half below.

But as for the provisions, we don't get half enough;
A little piece of stinking beef and a blamed small bag of duff.

Now comes that damned old compass, it will grieve your heart
    full sore.
For theirs is two-and-thirty points and we have forty-four.

Next comes the running rigging, which you're all supposed to
    know;
'Tis "Lay aloft, you son-of-a-gun, or overboard you go!"

The cooper's at the vise-bench, a-making iron poles,
And the mate's upon the main hatch a-cursing all our souls.

The Skipper's on the quarter-deck a-squinting at the sails,
When up aloft the lookout sights a school of whales.

"Now clear away the boats, my boys, and after him we'll travel,
But if you get too near his fluke, he'll kick you to the devil!"

Now we have got him turned up, we tow him alongside;
We over with our blubber-hooks and rob him of his hide.

Now the boat-steerer overside the tackle overhauls,
The Skipper's in the main-chains, so loudly does he bawl!

Next comes the stowing down, my boys; 'twill take both night
and day,
And you'll all have fifty cents apiece on the hundred and nine-
tieth lay.

Now we are bound into Tonbas, that blasted whaling port,
And if you run away, my boys, you surely will get caught.

Now we are bound into Tuckoona, full more in their power,
Where the skippers can buy the Consul up for half a barrel of
flour!

But now that our old ship is full and we don't give a damn,
We'll bend on all our stu'nsails and sail for Yankee land.

When we get home, our ship made fast, and we get through our
sailing,
A winding glass around we'll pass and damn this blubber whaling!

Song of the Fishes

Come all you bold fishermen, listen to me,
While I sing to you a song of the sea.

CHORUS: Then blow ye winds westerly, westerly blow,
We're bound to the southward, so steady we go.

129

First comes the blue-fish a-wagging his tail,
He comes up on deck and yells: "All hands make sail!"

Next come the eels, with their nimble tails,
They jumped up aloft and loosed all the sails.

Next come the herrings, with their little tails,
They manned sheets and halliards and set all the sails.

Next comes the porpoise, with his short snout,
He jumps on the bridge and yells: "Ready, about!"

Next comes the swordfish, the scourge of the sea,
The order he gives is "Helm's a-lee!"

Then comes the turbot, as red as a beet,
He shouts from the bridge: "Stick out that foresheet!"

Having accomplished these wonderful feats,
The blackfish sings out next to: "Rise tacks and sheets!"

Next comes the whale, the largest of all,
Singing out from the bridge: "Haul taut, mainsail, haul!"

Then comes the mackerel, with his striped back,
He flopped on the bridge and yelled: "Board the main tack!"

Next comes the sprat, the smallest of all,
He sings out: "Haul well taut, let go and haul!"

Then comes the catfish, with his chuckle head,
Out in the main chains for a heave of the lead.

Next comes the flounder, quite fresh from the ground,
Crying: "Damn your eyes, chucklehead, mind where you sound!"

Along came the dolphin, flapping his tail,
He yelled to the boatswain to reef the foresail.

Along came the shark, with his three rows of teeth,
He flops on the foreyard and takes a snug reef.

Up jumps the fisherman, stalwart and grim,
And with his big net he scooped them all in.

CHORUS: Then blow ye winds westerly, westerly blow,
We're bound to the southward, so steady we go.

Jack the Guinea Pig

When the anchor's weigh'd and the ship's unmoored,
And the landsmen lag behind, sir,
The sailor joyful skips aboard,
And, swearing, prays for a wind, sir!

Towing here,
Yehoing there,
Steadily, readily,
Cheerily, merrily,
Still from care and thinking free,
Is a sailor's life at sea.

When we sail with a fresh'ning breeze,
And the landsmen all grow sick, sir,
The sailor lolls, with his mind at ease,
And the song and the can go quick, sir!

Laughing here,
Quaffing there,
Steadily, readily, etc.

SWALLOWING THE ANCHOR

KEEP ON

When the wind at night whistles o'er the deep,
And sings to the landsmen dreary,
The sailor fearless goes to sleep,
Or takes his watch most cheery!

> *Boozing here,*
> *Snoozing there,*
> *Steadily, readily, etc.*

When the sky grows black and the wind blows hard,
And the landsmen skulk below, sir,
Jack mounts up to the top-sail yard,
And turns his quid as he goes, sir!

> *Hauling here,*
> *Bawling there,*
> *Steadily, readily, etc.*

When the foaming waves run mountains high,
And the landsmen cry, "All's gone, sir,"
The sailor hangs 'twixt sea and sky,
And he jokes with Davy Jones, sir!

> *Dashing here,*
> *Clashing there,*
> *Steadily, readily, etc.*

When the ship, d'ye see, becomes a wreck,
And the landsmen hoist the boat, sir,
The sailor scorns to quit the deck,
While a single plank's afloat, sir!

> *Swearing here,*
> *Tearing there,*
> *Steadily, readily,*
> *Cheerily, merrily,*
> *Still from care and thinking free,*
> *Is a sailor's life at sea.*

THE GIRL HE LEFT BEHIND

Spanish Ladies

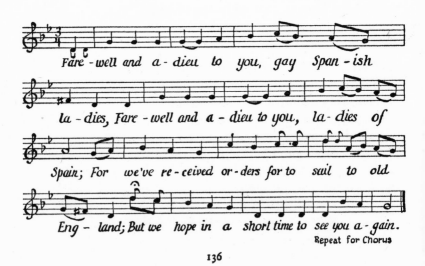

Fare-well and a-dieu to you, gay Span-ish la-dies, Fare-well and a-dieu to you, la-dies of Spain; For we've re-ceived or-ders for to sail to old Eng-land; But we hope in a short time to see you a-gain.

Repeat for Chorus

Farewell and adieu to you, gay Spanish ladies,
Farewell and adieu to you, ladies of Spain;
For we've received orders for to sail to old England;
But we hope in a short time to see you again.

We'll rant and we'll roar like true British sailors,
We'll rant and we'll roar across the salt seas,
Until we strike soundings in the channel of old England,
From Ushant to Scilly is thirty-five leagues.

Then we hove our ship to with the wind at sou'west, my boys,
We hove our ship to our soundings for to see;
So we rounded and sounded, and got forty-five fathoms,
We squared our mainyard, up channel steered we.

CHORUS

Now the first land we made it is called the Deadman,
Then, Ramshead off Plymouth, Start, Portland and Wight;
We passed by Beechy, by Fairleigh and Dungeness,
And hove our ship to, off South Foreland Light.

CHORUS

Then a signal was made for the grand fleet to anchor,
All in the Downs, that night for to meet;
Then stand by your stoppers, let go your shank-painters,
Haul all your clew garnets, stick out tacks and sheets.

CHORUS

So let every man toss off a full bumper,
Let every man toss off his full bowls;
We'll drink and be jolly and drown melancholy,
Singing, here's good health to all true-hearted souls.

I Am a Brisk and Sprightly Lad

I am a brisk and sprightly lad,
But just come home from sea, sir.
  Of all the lives I ever led,
  A sailor's life for me, sir.

    Yeo, yeo, yeo,
    Whilst the boatswain pipes all hands,
    With a yeo, yeo, yeo!

What girl but loves the merry tar,
We o'er the ocean roam, sir.
In every clime we find a port,
In every port a home, sir.

But when our country's foes are nigh,
Each hastens to his guns, sir.
We make the boasting Frenchman fly,
And bang the haughty Dons, sir.

Our foes reduced, once more on shore,
And spend our cash with glee, sir.
And when all's gone we drown our care,
And out to sea again, sir.

    Yeo, yeo, yeo,
    Whilst the boatswain pipes all hands,
    With a yeo, yeo, yeo!

HE WAS A GAY
AND
SPRIGHTLY LAD

Rolling Home

THIS BALLAD, so completely English, is a great favorite on the vessels of all nations. Several attempts have been made by eager patriots to give it a Yankee slant, such as "rolling home to dear old Boston" or to New York or some other two-syllable port but without any auricular success. Americans, letting go as the song deserves, still roll home to merry England.

Up a-loft a-mid the rig-ging, Swift-ly blows the fa-voring gale, Strong as spring-time in its blos-som, Fill-ing out each bend-ing sail. And the waves we leave be-hind us, Seem to mur-mur as they rise, We have tar-ried here to bear you To the land you dear-ly prize. Roll-ing home, roll-ing home, roll-ing home a-cross the sea; Roll-ing home to dear old Eng-land, Roll-ing home, dear land, to thee!

Up aloft amid the rigging,
Swiftly blows the favoring gale,
Strong as springtime in its blossom,
Filling out each bending sail.
And the waves we leave behind us,
Seem to murmur as they rise,
We have tarried here to bear you,
To the land you dearly prize.

    Rolling home, rolling home,
    Rolling home across the sea;
    Rolling home to dear old England,
    Rolling home, dear land, to thee!

Full ten thousand miles behind us,
And a thousand miles before,
Ancient ocean waves to waft us
To the well-remembered shore.
Newborn breezes swell to send us
To our childhood's welcome skies,
To the glow of friendly faces
And the glance of loving eyes.

    Rolling home, rolling home,
    Rolling home across the sea;
    Rolling home to dear old England,
    Rolling home, dear land, to thee!

Home, Dearie, Home

Included through the courtesy of Miss Joanna C. Colcord.*

Oh, Bos-ton's a fine town with ships in the bay, and
I wish in my heart it was there I was to-day, I
wish in my heart I was far a-way from here,

CHORUS

Sit-ting in my par-lor and talk-ing to my dear. Then it's
home, dear-ie, home, it's home I want to be and it's
home, dear-ie home, a-cross the rol-ling sea. Oh, the
oak and the ash and the bon-ny elm tree,
They're all a-grow-in' green in my own coun-try.

Oh, Boston's a fine town, with ships in the bay,
And I wish in my heart it was there I was today,
I wish in my heart I was far away from here,
A-sitting in my parlor and talking to my dear.

Then it's home, dearie, home, it's home I want to be,
And it's home, dearie, home, across the rolling sea,
Oh, the oak and the ash and the bonny ellum tree,
They're all a-growin' green in my own countree.

In Baltimore a-walking a lady I did meet,
With her baby on her arm as she walked down the street,
And I thought how I sailed, and the cradle standing ready,
And the pretty little babe that has never seen its daddy.

CHORUS

And if it's a girl, oh, she shall live with me,
And if it's a boy, he shall sail the rolling sea;
With his tarpaulin hat and his little jacket blue,
He shall walk the quarter-deck as his daddy used to do.

W. E. Henley, the English poet, liked the song so well that he
changed it to read Falmouth instead of Boston and the bonny elm
tree became the birken tree. In the third verse he tosses the as yet
unborn child right onto the deck of the Royal Navy:

O, if it be a lass, she shall wear a golden ring;
And if it be a lad, he shall fight for his king:
With his dirk and his hat and his little jacket blue,
He shall walk the quarter-deck as his daddy used to do.

The American Navy has a roistering version of the chorus:

Home, boys, home, it's home we ought to be!
Home, boys, home, in God's countree!
The apple and the oak and the weeping willow tree,
Green grows the grass in North Amerikee!

And lastly it became the many-versioned "Bell-Bottom Trousers" of the clubhouses and bull sessions.

Bell-Bottom Trousers

When I was a serving maid, down in Drury Lane,
My master was so kind to me, my mistress was the same.
Then came a sailor, home from the sea,
And he was the cause of all my misery.

Singing *

Bell-bottom trousers, coat of navy blue,
He can climb the rigging as his daddy used to do.

He asked for a candle to light him up to bed,
He asked for a pillow to place beneath his head;
And I, like a silly girl, thinking it no harm,
Jumped into the sailor's bed to keep the sailor warm.

Singing

Bell-bottom trousers, coat of navy blue,
He can climb the rigging as his daddy used to do.

Early in the morning, before the break of day,
He handed me a five-pound note and this to me did say:
"Maybe you'll have a daughter, maybe you'll have a son,
Take this, my darling, for the damage I have done."

Singing

Bell-bottom trousers, coat of navy blue,
He can climb the rigging as his daddy used to do.

"If you have a daughter, bounce her on your knee,
But if you have a son send the rascal out to sea.
Singing bell-bottom trousers, coat of navy blue,
He'll climb the rigging as his daddy used to do."

* Spoken flatly.

Homeward Bound

To Pensacola town we'll bid adieu,
To lovely Kate and pretty Sue.
Our anchor's weighed and our sails unfurled,
We're bound for to plough this watery world.

You know we're outward bound,
Hurrah, we're outward bound!

The wind blows hard from the east-nor'east,
Our ship sails ten knots at least,
The skipper will our wants supply,
And while we've grog we'll ne'er say die.

And should we touch at Malabar,
Or any other port so far,
Our skipper will tip the chink,
And just like fishes we will drink.

And now our three years it is out,
It's very near time we back'd about;
And when we're home, and do get free,
Oh, won't we have a jolly spree.

You know we're homeward bound,
Hurrah, we're homeward bound!

And now we'll haul into the docks,
Where all the pretty girls come in flocks,
And one to the other they will say,
"Here comes Jack with his three years' pay!"

And now we'll haul to the "Dog and Bell,"
Where there's good liquor for to sell,
In comes old Archer with a smile,
Saying, "Drink, my lads, it's worth your while."

But when our money's all gone and spent,
And none to be borrowed nor none to be lent,
In comes old Archer with a frown,
Saying, "Get up, Jack, let John sit down.

I know you're outward bound."
Hurrah, we're outward bound!

CROSSING THE LINE

HOME FOR CHRISTMAS

Wardroom Ballads

TAKING. A PRIZE

The Yankee Man-of-War

Sometimes The Stately Southerner

AMERICAN SAILORMEN have taken over many songs that were written for the patriotic uses of the British. There is one American song that survives principally because of its popularity among the English, who seem to prefer the title "The Stately Southerner."

Cruising in the *Ranger*, eighteen guns, Captain John Paul Jones, in 1778, conducted a series of punishing raids on the English coast, capturing merchantmen, burning the shipping at White-haven and other points, and finally taking captive the British twenty-gun *Drake* that had been sent out to stop him. The British sent more and bigger ships, and the song celebrates the *Ranger's* escape.

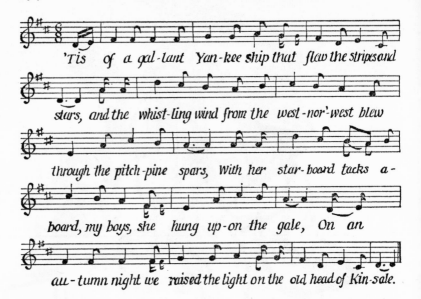

'Tis of a gallant Yankee ship that flew the stripes and stars,
And the whistling wind from the west-nor'west blew through the
  pitch-pine spars,
With her starboard tacks aboard, my boys, she hung upon the gale,
On an autumn night we raised the light on the old head of Kinsale.

It was a clear and cloudless night, and the wind blew steady and
  strong,
As gayly over the sparkling deep our good ship bowled along;
With the foaming seas beneath her bow the fiery waves she spread,
And bending low her bosom of snow, she buried her lee cat-head.

There was no talk of short'ning sail by him who walked the poop,
And under the press of her pond'ring jib, the boom bent like a
  hoop!
And the groaning waterways told the strain that held her stout
  main-tack,
But he only laughed as he glanced abaft at a white and silv'ry track.

A DAY AT THE SEA SHORE

The mid-tide meets in the channel waves that flow from shore to
    shore,
And the mist hung heavy upon the land from Featherstone to Dun-
    more,
And that sterling light in Tusker Rock where the old bell tolls
    each hour,
And the beacon light that shone so bright was quench'd on Water-
    ford Tower.

The nightly robes our good ship wore were her own topsails
    three,
Her spanker and her standing jib—the courses being free;
"Now, lay aloft! my heroes bold, let not a moment pass!"
And royals and topgallant sails were quickly on each mast.

What looms upon our starboard bow? What hangs upon the
    breeze?
'Tis time our good ship hauled her wind abreast the old Saltee's.
For by her ponderous press of sail and by her consorts four
We saw our morning visitor was a British man-of-war.

Up spoke our noble Captain then, as a shot ahead of us past—
"Haul snug your flowing courses! lay your topsail to the mast!"
Those Englishmen gave three loud hurrahs from the deck of their
    covered ark,
And we answered back by a solid broadside from the decks of our
    patriot bark.

"Out booms! out booms!" our skipper cried, "out booms and give
    her sheet,"
And the swiftest keel that was ever launched shot ahead of the
    British fleet,
And amidst a thundering shower of shot with stun'sails hoisting
    away,
Down the North Channel Paul Jones did steer just at the break of
    day.

Ye Parliament of England

War of 1812

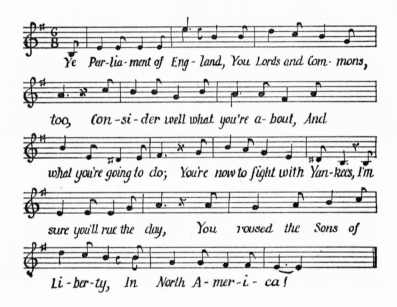

Ye Par-lia-ment of Eng-land, You Lords and Com-mons, too, Con-si-der well what you're a-bout, And what you're going to do; You're now to fight with Yan-kees, I'm sure you'll rue the day, You roused the Sons of Li-ber-ty, In North A-mer-i-ca!

Ye Parliament of England,
    You Lords and Commons, too,
Consider well what you're about,
    And what you're going to do;
You're now to fight with Yankees,
    I'm sure you'll rue the day,
You roused the Sons of Liberty,
    In North America!

You first confined our commerce,
    And said our ships shan't trade,
You next impressed our seamen,
    And used them as your slaves;
You then insulted Rodgers,
    While ploughing o'er the main,
And had we not declared war,
    You'd have done it o'er again!

You thought our frigates were but few
    And Yankees could not fight,
Until brave Hull your *Guerrière* took
    And banished her from your sight.
The *Wasp* then took your *Frolic*,
    We'll nothing say to that,
The *Poictiers* being of the line,
    Of course she took her back.

The next, your *Macedonian*,
    No finer ship could swim,
Decatur took her gilt-work off,
    And then he sent her in.
The *Java*, by a Yankee ship
    Was sunk, you all must know;
The *Peacock* fine, in all her plume,
    By Lawrence down did go.

Then next you sent your *Boxer*,
    To box us all about,
But we had an *Enterprising* brig
    That beat your *Boxer* out;
We boxed her up to Portland,
    And moored her off the town,
To show the Sons of Liberty
    The *Boxer* of renown.

The next upon Lake Erie,
　Where Perry had some fun,
You own he beat your naval force,
　And caused them for to run;
This was to you a sore defeat,
　The like ne'er known before—
Your British squadron beat complete—
　Some took, some run ashore.

There's Rodgers, in the *President*,
　Will burn, sink, and destroy;
The *Congress*, on the Brazil coast,
　Your commerce will annoy;
The *Essex*, in the South Seas,
　Will put out all your lights,
The flag she waves at her mast-head—
　"Free Trade and Sailors' Rights."

Lament, ye Sons of Britain,
　For distant is the day,
When you'll regain by British force,
　What you've lost in America;
Go tell your king and parliament,
　By all the world 'tis known,
That British force, by sea and land,
　By Yankees is o'erthrown!

Use every endeavor,
　And strive to make a peace,
For Yankee ships are building fast,
　Their navy to increase;
They will enforce their commerce;
　The laws by heaven are made,
That Yankee ships in time of peace
　To any port may trade.

The *Constitution* and the *Guerrière*

OF ALL OUR wars, that of 1812 was the most productive of
songs: the naval songsters are full of them, and even at this late
date many are still in favor in the wardrooms of the Navy. The
old charge so often leveled against Americans that they are over-
boastful has much in it save when uttered by the British. There
were two great engagements in that war, the first won by the
Americans, the second by the British, and the reader can decide
which service crowed the loudest. Both songs were written to
the music of "A Drop of Brandy, O!"

The fight between the *Constitution* and the *Guerrière* took
place off the New England coast, August 19, 1812. In less than
half an hour the *Guerrière*, fifty guns, commanded by Captain
Dacres, was a wreck not worth towing to port and was blown
up. The *Constitution*, forty-four guns, was commanded by Captain Isaac Hull. It was in this battle that the American sailors, see-
ing the solid British shot bouncing off the live oak sides of their
vessel, named her "Old Ironsides."

It oft-times has been told, That the British sea-man bold Could flog the tars of France so neat and han-dy, oh! But they ne-ver found their match, Till the Yan-kees did them catch, Oh the Yan-kee boys for fight-ing are the dan-dy, oh!

It ofttimes has been told,
That the British seaman bold
Could flog the tars of France so neat and handy, oh!
But they never found their match,
Till the Yankees did them catch,
Oh, the Yankee boys for fighting are the dandy, oh!

The *Guerrière*, a frigate bold,
On the foaming ocean rolled,
Commanded by proud Dacres the grandee, oh!
With as choice an English crew,
As a rammer ever drew,
Could flog the Frenchmen two to one so handy, oh!

When this frigate hove in view,
Says proud Dacres to his crew,
"Come, clear ship for action and be handy, oh!
To the weather gage, boys, get her,"
And to make his men fight better,
Gave them to drink, gunpowder mixed with brandy, oh!

Then Dacres loudly cries,
    "Make this Yankee ship your prize,
You can in thirty minutes, neat and handy, oh!
    Twenty-five's enough I'm sure,
    And if you'll do it in a score,
I'll treat you to a double share of brandy, oh!"

The British shot flew hot,
    Which the Yankee answered not,
Till they got within the distance they called handy, oh!
    "Now," says Hull unto his crew,
    "Boys, let's see what we can do,
If we take this boasting Briton we're the dandy, oh!"

The first broadside we poured
    Carried her mainmast by the board,
Which made this lofty frigate look abandoned, oh!
    Then Dacres shook his head,
    And to his officers said,
"Lord! I didn't think those Yankees were so handy, oh!"

Our second told so well,
    That their fore and mizzen fell,
Which dous'd the royal ensign neat and handy, oh!
    "By George," says he, "we're done,"
    And they fired a lee gun,
While the Yankees struck up Yankee Doodle Dandy, oh!

Then Dacres came on board,
    To deliver up his sword,
Tho' loath he was to part with it, it was so handy, oh!
    "Oh, keep your sword," says Hull,
    "For it only makes you dull,
Cheer up and let us have a little brandy, oh!"

Now fill your glasses full,
And we'll drink to Captain Hull,
And so merrily we'll push about the brandy, oh!
John Bull may toast his fill,
But let the world say what they will,
The Yankee boys for fighting are the dandy, oh!

The following year, on June first, while the *Chesapeake*, Captain James Lawrence, was lying in Boston Harbor, the *Shannon*, Captain P. V. Broke, came up with the express design of fighting the American. Captain Lawrence accepted the challenge and sailed out to meet the enemy. He and his chief officers were mortally wounded, and it was at this moment that Lawrence uttered his immortal words, "Don't give up the ship!" Carried to his cabin, he said: "Go on deck and order them to fire faster and fight the ship till she sinks. Never strike. Let the colors wave while I live." But the *Chesapeake* was taken by assault and Lawrence carried a prisoner to Halifax, where he died.

The *Shannon* and the *Chesapeake*

Included through the courtesy of Arch H. Ferguson. *

Now the *Chesapeake* so bold
Sailed from Boston we've been told,
For to take the British frigate neat and handy, O!
   The people in the port
   All came out to see the sport
And the bands were playing "Yankee Doodle Dandy, O!"

The British frigate's name,
Which for the purpose came
To cool the Yankee courage neat and handy-o,
   Was the *Shannon*—Captain Broke,
   All her men were hearts of oak.
And at fighting were allowed to be the dandy-o.

* From *Sea Songs and Shanties*, collected by W. B. Whall. **Fourth Edition.**
Published by Brown, Son & Ferguson, Ltd., Glasgow.

The fight had scarce begun
Ere they flinch-ed from their guns,
Which at first they started working neat and handy-o.
Then brave Broke he waved his sword,
Crying, "Now, my lads, aboard,
And we'll stop their playing 'Yankee Doodle Dandy-o.' "

They no sooner heard the word,
Than they quickly jumped aboard,
And hauled down the Yankee colours neat and handy-o;
Notwithstanding all their brag,
Now the glorious British flag
At the Yankee mizzen peak was quite the dandy-o.

Here's a health, brave Broke, to you,
To your officers and crew,
Who aboard the *Shannon* frigate fought so handy-o;
And may it always prove,
That in fighting and in love,
The British tar forever is the dandy-o.

Charge the Can Cheerily

Copied from the original in the Public Library of the City of Boston

Now coil up your nonsense 'bout England's great Navy,
    And take in your slack about oak-hearted Tars;
For frigates as stout, and as gallant crews have we,
    Or how came her *Macedon* deck'd with our stars?
Yes—how came her *Guerrière*, her *Peacock*, and *Java*,
    All sent broken ribb'd to Old Davy of late?
How came it? why, split me! than Britons we're braver,
    And that shall they feel it whenever we meet.

CHORUS: *Then charge the can cheerily;*
          Send it round merrily;
    Here's to our country and captains commanding;
          To all who inherit
          Of Lawrence the spirit,
    "Disdaining to strike while a stick is left standing."

Now coil up your non-sense 'bout Eng-land's great Na-vy, And take in your slack a-bout oak-heart-ed Tars; For fri-gates as stout, and as gal-lant crews have we, Or how came her Ma-ce-don deck'd with our stars? Yes,—how came her Guer-riere, her Pea-cock, and Ja-va, All sent bro-ken ribb'd to Old Da-vy of late? How came it? Why, split me! than Bri-tons we're bra-ver, And that shall they feel it wher-ev-er we meet. Then charge the can

CHORUS

cheer-i-ly; Send it round mer-ri-ly: Here's to our coun-try and cap-tains com-mand-ing; To all who in-her-it of Law-rence the spir-it, "Dis-dain-ing to strike while a stick is left stand-ing."

Now, if unawares, we should run (a fresh gale in)
    Close in with a squadron, we'd laugh at 'em all;
We'd tip master Bull such a sample of sailing,
    As should cause him to fret like a pig in a squall;
We'd show the vain boaster of numbers superior,
    Though he and his slaves at the notion may sneer,
In skill, as in courage, to us they're inferior;
    For the longer they chase us the less we've to fear.

CHORUS

But should a Razee be espied ahead nearly;
    To fetch her we'd crowd ev'ry stitch we could make;
Down chests and up hammocks would heave away cheerily,
    And ready for action would be in a shake;
For her swaggering cut, though, and metal not caring,
    Till up with her close should our fire be withheld;
Then pour'd in so hot that her mangled crew, fearing
    A trip to the bottom, should speedily yield.

CHORUS

Britannia, although she beleaguers our coast now,
    The dread of our wives and our sweethearts as well,
Of ruling the waves has less reason to boast now,
    As Dacres, and Carden, and Whinyates can tell:
Enroll'd in our annals live Hull and Decatur,
    Jones, Lawrence, and Bainbridge, Columbia's pride;
The pride of our Navy, which sooner or later,
    Shall on the wide ocean triumphantly ride.

    Then charge the can cheerily;
    Send it round merrily;
Here's to our country and captains commanding;
    To all who inherit
    Of Lawrence the spirit,
"Disdaining to strike while a stick is left standing."

Nancy Lee

Of all the wives as e'er you know, Yeo-

ho! lads, ho! Yeo-ho! Yeo-ho! There's none like

Nan-cey Lee, I trow, Yeo-ho! Yeo-ho! Yeo-

ho! See there she stands and waves her hands up-on the

quay, And ev-ery day when I'm a-way she'll watch for

me, And whis-per low when tem-pests blow, for Jack at

sea, Yeo-ho! lads, ho! Yeo-ho! The sail-or's

wife, the sail-or's star shall be, Yeo-ho! We go a-

cross the sea, the sail-or's wife the sail-or's star shall

be, The sail-or's wife his star shall be!

Of all the wives as e'er you know,
   Yeo-ho! lads, ho! Yeo-ho! Yeo-ho!
There's none like Nancy Lee, I trow,
   Yeo-ho! Yeo-ho! Yeo-ho!
See there she stands and waves her hands upon the quay,
And every day when I'm away she'll watch for me,
And whisper low when tempests blow, for Jack at sea,
   Yeo-ho! lads, ho! Yeo-ho!

CHORUS

   The sailor's wife the sailor's star shall be,
      Yeo-ho! We go across the sea;
   The sailor's wife the sailor's star shall be,
   The sailor's wife his star shall be!

The harbor's past, the breezes blow,
   Yeo-ho! lads, ho! Yeo-ho! Yeo-ho!
'Tis long ere we come back, I know.
   Yeo-ho! Yeo-ho! Yeo-ho!
But true and bright from morn till night my home will be,
And all so neat, and snug and sweet, for Jack at sea,
And Nancy's face to bless the place, and welcome me.
   Yeo-ho! lads, ho! Yeo-ho!

CHORUS

The bosun pipes the watch below,
   Yeo-ho! lads, ho! Yeo-ho! Yeo-ho!
Then here's a health afore we go,
   Yeo-ho! Yeo-ho! Yeo-ho!
A long, long life to my sweet wife, and mates at sea,
And keep our bones from Davy Jones, where-e'er we be,
And may you meet a mate as sweet as Nancy Lee.
   Yeo-ho! lads, ho! Yeo-ho!

The Norfolk Girls

Our top-sails reef'd and filled a-way, All snug a-loft we know, De-spite the storm we'll still be gay, A-mong our friends be-low. Come ga-ther round and lis-ten, then, with spi-rits warm and true; Here's a health to all the Nor-folk girls, And

CHORUS

Ports-mouth maid-ens, too. Here's a health to all the Nor-folk girls, And Ports-mouth maid-ens, too, There's a health to all the Nor-folk girls, And Ports-mouth maid-ens, too.

Sir Henry Morgan

NEXT IS SIR HENRY ~

Our topsails reef'd and filled away,
All snug aloft we know,
Despite the storms we'll still be gay,
Among our friends below.
Come gather round and listen, then,
With spirits warm and true;
Here's a health to all the Norfolk girls,
And Portsmouth maidens, too.

Here's a health to all the Norfolk girls,
And Portsmouth maidens, too,
Here's a health to all the Norfolk girls,
And Portsmouth maidens, too.

May the darksome eye of loveliness,
And that of ocean's ray,
Shed only tears of happiness
Forever and for aye.
Fill up, tho' far away from home,
And foreign scenes we view,
We cherish still the Norfolk girls,
And the Portsmouth maidens, too.

CHORUS

May the cheek whereon reposes
Emotion young and dear,
Still wear the hue of roses
Thro' each succeeding year.
We'll drink to by-past scenes, and hope
Some day again to view,
The lovely girls of Norfolk, and
The Portsmouth maidens, too.

CHORUS

And if we never backward go,
Borne home on ocean's breast,

But find among the caves below
A sailor's place of rest;
Still ere we close our eyes and pass
Beneath the depths of blue,
We'll think of all the Norfolk girls,
And Portsmouth maidens, too.

CHORUS

Should the foe appear before us,
To our guns we'll fondly cling,
While our stars are gleaming o'er us,
Shall their notes of freedom ring.
While life's warm stream is flowing,
Our eager pulses through,
We'll fight for home, the Norfolk girls,
And Portsmouth maidens, too.

CHORUS

Fill up, fill up, yet once again,
Before we say good night,
From every glass its sweetness drain,
To friendship's steady light.
May peace around our kindred dwell,
All beings loved and true,
The lovely girls of Norfolk,
And the Portsmouth maidens, too.

CHORUS

Good night, good night, our pillows now
With pleasant thoughts we'll press,
And dream some hand rests on our brow,
Its slumbering to bless.
Amid delightful reveries
That fancy brings to view,

Perhaps we'll meet the Norfolk girls,
And Portsmouth maidens, too.

Here's a health to all the Norfolk girls,
  And Portsmouth maidens, too,
Here's a health to all the Norfolk girls,
  And Portsmouth maidens, too.

The Flash Frigate

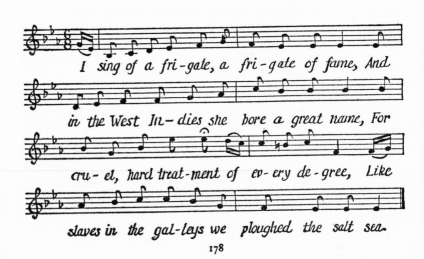

I sing of a fri-gate, a fri-gate of fame, And
in the West In-dies she bore a great name, For
cru-el, hard treat-ment of ev-ery de-gree, Like
slaves in the gal-leys we ploughed the salt sea.

I sing of a frigate, a frigate of fame,
And in the West Indies she bore a great name,
For cruel, hard treatment of every degree,
Like slaves in the galleys we ploughed the salt sea.

At four in the morning our day's work begun;
"Come, lash up your hammocks, boys, every one."
Seven turns with the lashing so neatly must show,
And all of one size through a hoop they must go.

The next thing we do is to holystone the decks,
Mizzen-topmen from the forehatch their buckets must fetch,
And its fore and main topmen so loudly they bawl,
Come, fetch up your holystones, squilgees and all.

The decks being scrubbed and the rigging coiled down,
It's clean up your bright work which is found all around,
Your gun-caps and aprons so neatly must shine,
And in white frocks and trousers you must all toe the line.

The next thing we hear is "All hands to make sail!"
"Way aloft!" and "Lay out!" and "Let fall!" is the hail,
Oh, your royals and your skysails and moonsails so high,
At the sound of the call your skyscrapers must fly.

But now, my brave boys, comes the best of the fun:
"All hands about ship and reef topsails," in one.
Oh, it's "lay aloft, topmen," as the helm goes down,
And it's "clew down your topsails," as the mainyard swings round.

"Trice up, and lay out, and take two snug reefs in one,"
And all in one moment this work must be done.
Then man your head braces, topsail-halliards and all,
And hoist away topsails as you let go and haul.

Our second lieutenant, you all know him well,
He comes up on deck and cuts a great swell.
Oh, it's "bear a hand here," and "bear a hand there."
And at the lee gangway he serves out our share.*

Now, all you bold seamen who plough the salt sea,
Beware this frigate wherever she be,
For they'll beat you and bang you till you ain't worth a damn,
And send you an invalid to your own native land.

H.M.S. *Pique*, frigate, was assigned for many years to the West
Indies station. She had the name of a "blood ship," and her vices
were celebrated chiefly by the American Navy.

* of the rope's end.

Miscellaneous Songs
and Ballads

The *Flying Cloud*

THIS BALLAD achieved a certain degree of popularity in the
shore dives and music halls patronized by sailormen that it never
deserved. The *Flying Cloud*, without doubt the greatest of the
clippers, was never in the slave trade nor given to piratical prac-
tices: her life is an open book and an inspiring one to all Americans.
No captain named Moore ever commanded her, and there are no
records of another ship with the same name. The song's closing
lines are reminiscent of "The Ballad of Captain Kidd," which follows it.

My name is Edward Hallahan and you must understand,
I came from County Waterford and Ireland's happy land.
When I was young and in my prime, fair fortune on me smiled,
My parents reared me tenderly, I was their only child.

My name is Ed-ward Hall-a-han and you must un-der-
stand, I came from Coun-ty Wa-ter-ford and
Ire-land's hap-py land. When I was young and
in my prime, fair for-tune on me smiled, My
pa-rents reared me ten-der-ly, 'I' was their on-ly child.

My father bound me to a trade in Waterford's fair town,
He bound me to a cooper there, by name of William Brown,
I served my master faithfully for eighteen months or more,
Then I shipped on board the *Ocean Queen*, belonging to Tramore.

When we came unto Bermuda's isle, there I met with Captain
    Moore,
The commander of The *Flying Cloud*, hailing from Baltimore.
He asked me if I'd ship with him, on a slaving voyage to go,
To the burning shores of Africa, where the sugar cane does grow.

It was after some weeks' sailing we arrived on Africa's shore,
Five hundred of those poor slaves, from their native land we tore,
We made them walk in on a plank, and we stowed them down
    below
Scarce eighteen inches to a man was all they had to go.

The plague and fever came on board, swept half of them away;
We dragged the bodies up on deck and hove them in the sea.
It was better for the rest of them that they had died before,
Than to work under brutes of planters in Cuba forevermore.

It was after stormy weather we arrived off Cuba's shore,
And we sold them to the planters there to be slaves forevermore.
For the rice and the coffee seed to sow beneath the broiling sun,
There to lead a wretched lonely life till their career was run.

It's now our money is all spent, we must go to sea again,
When Captain Moore he came on deck and said unto us men:
"There is gold and silver to be had if with me you'll remain,
And we'll hoist the pirate flag aloft and scour the Spanish Main."

We all agreed but three young men who told us them to land,
And two of them were Boston boys, the other from Newfound-
    land.
I wish to God I'd joined those men and went with them on shore,
Than to lead a wild and reckless life, serving under Captain Moore.

The *Flying Cloud* was a Yankee ship of five hundred tons or more,
She could outsail any clipper ship hailing out of Baltimore.
With her canvas white as driven snow, and on it there's no specks,
And forty men and fourteen guns she carried on her decks.

It's oft I've seen that gallant ship with the wind abaft her beam,
With her royals and her stunsails set, a sight for to be seen;
With the curling waves at her clipper bow, a sailor's joy to feel,
And the canvas taut in the whistling breeze, logging fourteen off
    the reel.

We sank and plundered many a ship down on the Spanish Main,
Caused many a wife and orphan in sorrow to remain;
To them we gave no quarter, but gave them watery graves
For the saying of our captain was, that dead men tell no tales.

Pursued we were by many a ship, by frigates and liners, too,
Till at last a British man-of-war, the *Dungeness*, hove in view;
She fired a shot across our bow, as we sailed before the wind,
Then a chain shot cut our mainmast down and we fell far behind.

Our crew they beat to quarters as she ranged up alongside,
And soon across our quarter-deck there ran a crimson tide.
We fought till Captain Moore was killed and twenty of our men,
Till a bombshell set our ship on fire; we had to surrender then.

It's next to Newgate we were brought, bound down in iron chains,
For the sinking and the plundering of ships on the Spanish Main.
The judge he found us guilty, we were condemned to die;
Young men, a warning take by me, and shun all piracy.

Then fare you well, old Waterford, and the girl that I adore,
I'll never kiss your cheek again, or squeeze your hand no more.
For whiskey and bad company first made a wretch of me;
Young men, a warning by me take, and shun all piracy.

The Ballad of Captain Kidd

My name was William Kidd, when I sailed, when I sailed,
　My name was William Kidd, when I sailed,
My name was William Kidd; God's laws I did forbid,
　And so wickedly I did, when I sailed.

My parents taught me well, when I sailed, when I sailed,
　My parents taught me well, when I sailed,
My parents taught me well, to shun the gates of hell,
　But against them I rebelled, when I sailed.

I'd a Bible in my hand, when I sailed, when I sailed,
　I'd a Bible in my hand, when I sailed,
I'd a Bible in my hand, by my father's great command,
　And I sunk it in the sand, when I sailed.

I murdered William Moore, as I sailed, as I sailed,
  I murdered William Moore, as I sailed,
I murdered William Moore, and laid him in his gore,
  Not many leagues from shore, as I sailed.

I was sick and nigh to death, as I sailed, as I sailed,
  I was sick and nigh to death, as I sailed,
I was sick and nigh to death and I vowed with every breath,
  To walk in wisdom's ways, when I sailed.

I thought I was undone, as I sailed, as I sailed,
  I thought I was undone, as I sailed,
I thought I was undone, and my wicked glass had run,
  But health did soon return, as I sailed.

My repentance lasted not, as I sailed, as I sailed,
  My repentance lasted not, as I sailed,
My repentance lasted not, my vows I soon forgot,
  Damnation was my lot, as I sailed.

I spied three ships from France, as I sailed, as I sailed,
  I spied three ships of France, as I sailed,
I spied the ships of France, to them I did advance,
  And took them all by chance, as I sailed.

I spied three ships from Spain, as I sailed, as I sailed,
  I spied three ships from Spain, as I sailed,
I spied the ships of Spain, I looted them for gain,
  Till most of them were slain, as I sailed.

I'd ninety bars of gold, as I sailed, as I sailed,
  I'd ninety bars of gold, as I sailed,
I'd ninety bars of gold and dollars manifold,
  With riches uncontrolled, as I sailed.

Thus being o'ertaken at last, as I sailed, as I sailed,
  Thus being o'ertaken at last, as I sailed,
Thus being o'ertaken at last, and into prison cast,
  And sentence being passed, I must die.

Farewell, the raging main, I must die, I must die,
    Farewell, the raging main, I must die,
Farewell, the raging main, to Turkey, France and Spain,
    I shall never see you again, for I must die.

To the Execution Dock, I must go, I must go,
    To the Execution Dock, I must go,
To the Execution Dock, while many thousands flock,
    But I must bear the shock, and must die.

Come all ye young and old and see me die, see me die,
    Come all ye young and old and see me die,
Come all ye young and old, you're welcome to my gold,
    For by it I've lost my soul, and must die.

Take a warning now by me, for I must die, I must die,
    Take a warning now by me, for I must die,
Take a warning now by me and shun bad company,
    Lest you come to hell with me, for I must die.

The Female Smuggler

Included through the courtesy of Arch H. Ferguson.*

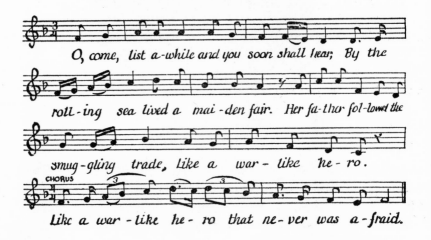

O, come, list a-while and you soon shall hear; By the

roll - ing sea lived a mai - den fair. Her fa-ther fol-lowed the

smug - gling trade, like a war - like he - ro.

CHORUS

Like a war - like he - ro that ne - ver was a - fraid.

O, come, list awhile, and you soon shall hear,
By the rolling sea lived a maiden fair.
Her father followed the smuggling trade,
Like a war-like hero.

Chorus: Like a war-like hero that never was afraid.

* From *Sea Songs and Shanties*, collected by W. B. Whall. Fourth Edition.
Published by Brown, Son & Ferguson, Ltd., Glasgow.

BLACKBEARD!

Now, in sailor's clothing young Jane did go,
Dressed like a sailor from top to toe;
Her aged father was the only care
Of this female smuggler,

Of this female smuggler who never did despair.

With her pistols loaded she went aboard.
And by her side hung a glittering sword,
In her belt two daggers; well armed for war
Was this female smuggler,

Was this female smuggler, who never feared a scar.

Now they had not sail-ed far from the land,
When a strange sail brought them to a stand.
"These are sea robbers," this maid did cry,
"But the female smuggler,

But the female smuggler will conquer or will die."

Alongside, then, this strange vessel came.
"Cheer up," cried Jane, "we will board the same;
We'll run all chances to rise or fall,"
Cried this female smuggler,

Cried this female smuggler who never feared a ball.

Now they killed these pirates and took their store,
And soon returned to old Eng-a-land's shore.
With a keg of brandy she walked along,
Did this female smuggler,

Did this female smuggler, and sweetly sang a song.

Now they were followed by the blockade,
Who in irons strong did put this fair maid.

But when they brought her for to be ter-ried,
This young female smuggler,

This young female smuggler stood dress-ed like a bride.

Their commodore against her appeared,
And for her life she did greatly fear.
When he did find to his great surprise
'Twas a female smuggler,

'Twas a female smuggler had fought him in disguise.

He to the judge and the jury said,
"I cannot prosecute this maid,
Pardon for her on my knees I crave,
For this female smuggler,

For this female smuggler so valiant and so brave."

Then this commodore to her father went,
To gain her hand he asked his consent.
His consent he gained, so the commodore
And the female smuggler,

And the female smuggler are one for evermore.

Little Mohee

IT WOULD BE nothing short of criminal negligence to leave this ballad out of a book of sailors' songs, even if it could be proved that no deep-water sailor ever sang the song. So much for the sailors' loss: it is a great folksong and is sung in the Kentucky mountains, the Texas plains, and all along the Shining Mountains. It is also a great favorite among the sailors on the Great Lakes.

The words and music were taken from a recording in the Archive of American Folksong of the Library of Congress.

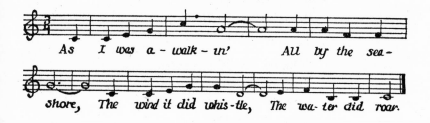

As I was a-walkin'
All by the seashore,
The wind it did whistle,
The water did roar.

As I sat a-musing
Myself on the grass,
Who should come by me
But a young Indian lass.

She came and sat by me,
Took hold of my hand,
And said, "You're a stranger
And in a strange land.

But if you will follow,
You're welcome to come
And dwell in the cottage
That I call my home."

The sun was past sinking
Far over the sea,
As I wandered along with
My little Mohee.

She asked me to marry
And offered her hand
Saying, "Father's the chieftain
All over this land.

My father's the chieftain
And ruler can be,
I'm his only daughter,
My name is Mohee."

"Oh, no, my dear maiden,
That never can be,
I have a dear sweetheart
In my own country.

I will not forsake her,
I know she loves me;
Her heart is as true
As any Mohee."

The last time I saw her
She knelt on the sand;
Just as my boat passed her
She waved me her hand.

Saying, "When you get over
With the girl that you love,
Remember the Mohee
In the mountains above."

And when I have landed
With the girl that I love,
Both friends and relations
Gathered 'round me once more.

I gazed all about me,
Not one did I see,
That did really compare
With my little Mohee.

The girl I had trusted
Proved untrue to me,
So I'll turn my courses
Back over the sea.

I'll turn my high courses,
Backwards I'll flee,
I'll go spend my days with
My little Mohee.

The Nantucket Skipper

NEW ENGLAND'S coast long had a fleet of packets, sloops, and schooners that operated between Boston and their home ports, carrying passengers, freight, and the mail. There are many stories of those rugged little vessels, but one, that of a Nantucket skipper, who day or night could remain in his bunk and give his position, is worth retelling. James T. Fields, a distinguished writer and editor, put it into verse.

Many a long, long year ago,
Nantucket skippers had a plan
Of finding out, though 'lying low,'
How near New York their schooners ran.

They greased the lead before it fell,
And then, by sounding through the night,
Knowing the soil that stuck, so well,
They always guessed their reckoning right.

A skipper gray, whose eyes were dim,
Could tell by *tasting*, just the spot;
And so below he'd dowse the glim,—
After, of course, his 'something hot.'

Snug in his berth, at eight o'clock,
This ancient skipper might be found.
No matter how his craft would rock,
He slept; for skippers' naps are sound.

The watch on deck would now and then
Run down and wake him, with the lead;
He'd up and taste, and tell the men
How many miles they went ahead.

One night 'twas Jotham Marden's watch,
A curious wag,—the pedler's son;
And so he mused (the wanton wretch):
"Tonight I'll have a grain of fun!

We're all a set of stupid fools
To think the skipper knows by *tasting*
What ground he's on,—Nantucket schools
Don't teach such stuff, with all their basting!"

And so he took the well-greased lead
And rubbed it o'er a box of earth
That stood on deck,—a parsnip bed;
And then he sought the skipper's berth.

"Where are we now, sir? Please to taste."
The skipper yawned, put out his tongue;
Then oped his eyes in wondrous haste,
And then upon the floor he sprung!

The skipper stormed and tore his hair,
Thrust on his boots, and roared to Marden:
"Nantucket's sunk, and here we are
Right over old Marm Hackett's garden."

Brother Noah

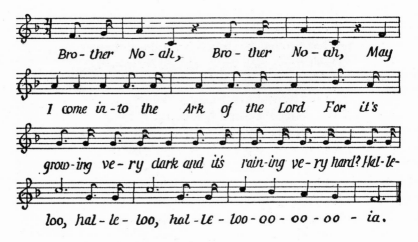

Bro-ther No-ah, Bro-ther No-ah, May
I come in-to the Ark of the Lord For it's
grow-ing ve-ry dark and it's rain-ing ve-ry hard? Hal-le-
loo, hal-le-loo, hal-le-loo-oo-oo-oo-ia.

Brother Noah, Brother Noah,
May I come into the Ark of the Lord
For it's growing very dark and it's raining very hard?
    Halleloo, halleloo, halleloo, hallelujah!

No, you can't sir, no, you can't, sir,
You can't come into the Ark of the Lord,
Though it's growing very dark and it's raining very hard.
    Halleloo, halleloo, halleloo, hallelujah!

Very well, sir, very well, sir,
You can go to the dickens with your darned old scow,
'Cause it ain't goin' to rain very hard anyhow.
　Halleloo, halleloo, halleloo, hallelujah!

That's a lie, sir, that's a lie, sir,
You can darn soon tell that it ain't no sell,
'Cause it's sprinklin' now and it's goin' to rain like hell.
　Halleloo, halleloo, halleloo, hallelujah!

The Girl I Left Behind Me

The dames of France are fond and free, And Flem-ish lips are

will-ing; And soft the maids of I-ta-ly, And

Span-ish eyes are thrill-ing; Still, though I bask be-

neath their smile, Their charms fail to bind me, And my

heart goes back to E-rins Isle, To the

girl I left be — hind me.

The dames of France are fond and free,
  And Flemish lips are willing;
And soft the maids of Italy,
  And Spanish eyes are thrilling;
Still, though I bask beneath their smile,
  Their charms fail to bind me.
And my heart goes back to Erin's Isle,
  To the girl I left behind me.

For she's as fair as Shannon's side,
  And purer than its water,
But she refused to be my bride
  Though many years I sought her.
Yet, since to France I sailed away,
  Her letters oft remind me,
That I promised never to gainsay
  The girl I left behind me.

She says: "My own dear love come home,
  My friends are rich and many;
Or else, abroad with you I'll roam,
  A soldier stout as any;
If you'll not come, nor let me go,
  I'll think you have resigned me."
My heart nigh broke when I answered "No,"
  To the girl I left behind me.

For never shall my true love brave
  A life of war and toiling,
And never as a skulking slave
  I'll tread my native soil on.
But were it free or to be freed,
  The battle's close would find me
To Ireland bound, nor message need
  From the girl I left behind me.

Rollicking Bill the Sailor

Who's that a-knocking at my door?
Cried the fair young maiden.
Who's that a-knocking at my door?
Cried the fair young maiden.

It's me, myself, and nobody else!
Cried Rollicking Bill the Sailor.
It's me, myself, and nobody else!
Cried Rollicking Bill the Sailor.

I'll come down and let you in,
Cried the fair young maiden.
I'll come down and let you in,
Cried the fair young maiden.

I need a place for me to sleep,
Cried Rollicking Bill the Sailor.
I need a place for me to sleep,
Cried Rollicking Bill the Sailor.

But we have only one bed!
Cried the fair young maiden.
But we have only one bed!
Cried the fair young maiden.

The Fire Ship*

As I strolled out one eve - ning, out for a night's ca - reer, I
spied a lof - ty fire - ship and af - ter her did steer. I
hoist - ed her my sig - a - nals which she ve - ry quick - ly knew; And
when she seed my bunt - ing fly she im - med - iate - ly hove
to - o - o. She's a dark and a rol - ling eye, And her
hair hung down in ring - a - lets. She was a nice girl, a
de - cent girl, But one of the ra - kish kind.

* From *Drawn from the Wood*. Copyright, 1929, by Frank Shay.

As I strolled out one evening, out for a night's career,
I spied a lofty fire ship and after her did steer.
I hoisted her my siganals which she very quickly knew;
And when she seed my bunting fly she immediately hove to.

CHORUS: She's a dark and rolling eye,
            And her hair hung down in ringalets.
            She was a nice girl, a decent girl,
            But one of the rakish kind.

"Oh, sir, you must excuse me for being out so late,
For if my parents knew of it, sad would be my fate.
My father he's a minister, a good and honest man,
My mother she's a Methodist, and I do the best I can."

CHORUS

I took her to a tavern and I treated her to wine,
Little did I think she belonged to the rakish kind.
I handled her, I dandled her, and found to my surprise,
She was nothing but a fire ship, rigged up in a disguise.

CHORUS

Christofo Columbo *

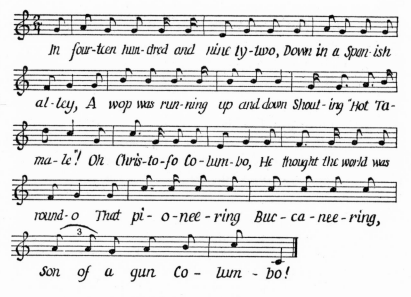

In fourteen hundred and ninety-two, Down in a Spanish alley, A wop was running up and down Shouting "Hot Tamale"! Oh Christofo Columbo, He thought the world was round-o That pi-o-nee-ring Buc-ca-nee-ring, Son of a gun Columbo!

In fourteen hundred and ninety-two,
Down in a Spanish alley,
A wop was running up and down
Shouting, "hot tamale!"

Oh, Christofo Columbo,
He thought the world was round-o;
That pioneering, buccaneering,
Son-of-a-gun, Columbo!

Columbus came from Italee,
  He was full of pink confetti;
He showed the Queen of Spain
  How to manage her spaghetti.

Oh, Christofo Columbo,
  Knew that land could be found-o;
That heathen-hating, navigating,
  Son-of-a-gun, Columbo!

He rushed up to the Queen one day,
  Said: "Give me ships and cargo,
I'll be a sea-going son-of-a-gun
  If I don't bring back Chicago!"

Oh, Christofo Columbo,
  He thought the world was round-o;
That encroaching, queen-approaching,
  Son-of-a-gun, Columbo!

The Queen she said to Ferdinand,
  "His scheme sounds like a daisy."
"To hell with him," said Ferdinand,
  "I think the wop is crazy!"

Oh, Christofo Columbo,
  He thought the world was round-o;
That pioneering, buccaneering,
  Son-of-a-gun, Columbo!

"It isn't ships or men he wants,
  For something else he's shootin',
And if he hangs around you much
  He'll lose his head right tootin'."

Oh, Christofo Columbo,
Knew the gold could be found-o;
That brave sea-faring, never-caring,
Son-of-a-gun, Columbo!

Said Columbo: "Now, Isabelle,
Don't act so gosh-darned funny;
I need the ships and men
So pony up the money!"

Oh, Christofo Columbo,
He knew ships could be found-o;
That always-busted, never trusted,
Son-of-a-gun, Columbo!

Said Isabelle: "Now wait awhile,
And cut out this flam-flimmin';
You've only asked for ships and men
But how about some wimmin?"

Oh, Christofo Columbo,
He knew the world was round-o;
This goll-durning, woman-spurning,
Son-of-a-gun, Columbo!

On the day they sailed away,
The people thought them crazy.
Columbus said: "No janes on board,
The sailors won't get lazy."

Oh, Christofo Columbo,
He never could be bound-o;
That woman-hating, captivating,
Son-of-a-gun, Columbo!

In fourteen hundred and ninety-two,
    Across the broad Atlantic;
The sailors all were filled with grief,
    Their wives were nearly frantic.

    Oh, Christofo Columbo,
    He knew the world was round-o;
    That family-breaking, history-making,
    Son-of-a-gun, Columbo!

In fourteen hundred and ninety-two,
    The doctors were not many;
The only one they had on board
    Was a gosh-darned quack named Benny.

    Oh, Christofo Columbo,
    He knew the world was round-o;
    That philosophic, philanthropic,
    Son-of-a-gun, Columbo!

Columbo's ears ached him one day,
    But Benny was quite placid.
He filled up both Columbo's ears
    With hot mercuric acid.

    Oh, Christofo Columbo,
    Knew doctors could be drowned-o;
    That democratic and autocratic,
    Son-of-a-gun, Columbo!

They anchored near San Salvydor,
    In search of women and booty;
A pretty girl stood on the shore,
    Columbo said: "Do your duty!"

Oh, Christofo Columbo,
Found here was solid ground-o;
That stop-your-shoving, woman-loving,
Son-of-a-gun, Columbo!

The sailors jumped into the surf,
    And shed their shirts and collars;
Columbo said: "The first one there
    Will get a hundred dollars."

Oh, Christofo Columbo,
Knew where he was bound-o;
That woman-baiting, captivating,
Son-of-a-gun, Columbo!

He settled down to stay awhile,
    But things were not so pretty;
The sailors started getting drunk
    Which really was a pity.

Oh, Christofo Columbo,
Got to where he was bound-o;
That heavy-headed, ever-dreaded,
Son-of-a-gun, Columbo!

One day they loaded him in chain,
    And shipped him back to Spain.
Columbo said: "I'm done for good,
    These doings give me a pain."

Oh, Christofo Columbo,
Proved the world was round-o;
That pioneering, persevering,
Son-of-a-gun, Columbo!

When Columbo got back to Sunny Spain,
He told them of bonanzas.
They answered him: "We notice, Wop,
You ain't got no bananas!"

Oh, Christofo Columbo,
He showed the world was round-o;
That poorly-treated, badly cheated,
Son-of-a-gun, Columbo!

ON LEAVE

REELING 'M OFF

Index of Songs

215

DATE DUE	
MAR 2 0 2007	
APR 1 0 2007	